On and On?

On and On?

Richard Ingrams and John Wells

Illustrated by Brian Bagnall

PRIVATE EYE · CORGI

Published in Great Britain
by Private Eye Productions Ltd,
6 Carlisle Street, London W1V 5RG
in association with Corgi Books

© 1990 Pressdram Ltd
Illustrations by Brian Bagnall © 1990
ISBN 0552 13750 8

Printed in Great Britain
by The Bath Press, Avon

Corgi Books are published by Transworld Publishers Ltd,
61–63 Uxbridge Road, Ealing, London W5 5SA,
in Australia by Transworld Publishers (Australia) Pty, Ltd,
15–23 Helles Avenue, Moorebank, NSW 2170
and in New Zealand by Transworld Publishers (N.Z.) Ltd,
Cnr. Moselle and Waipareira Avenues, Henderson, Auckland

10 Downing Street
Whitehall

Dear Bill,

You enquire in your last about my health following these ridiculous rumours about Mother Banerjee's Electric Bath. The fact is that I was persuaded to go there by the Mem, after a particularly heavy night with the Major and his friend Shorty Whittam-Smith (you remember, one eye, peg leg, terrible breath). I must have been looking pretty peaky over the lightly-boiled, as Margaret gripped me by the wrist and looked me straight in the eye, accusing me of letting myself go and saying that the whites of my eye matched the yellow of the egg. Before I could stammer out any explanation she was on the blower to some massage parlour in Shepherds Bush recommended by HM the Q as providing a pick-me-up for the Wrinkly Brigade at seven hundred quid a throw.

You remember that time we were in Tunis in '46 and went to a Turkish Bath run by the very fat woman Maurice was married to at one point? It sounded to me as if this was the same kind of caper, so naturally I agreed, in the interests of a quiet life. Picture my dismay on arrival in a rather seedy backstreet off the Uxbridge Road to be greeted by a menacing old Gypsy woman dripping in gold bangles and fancy jewellery, who took my hand in both of hers and led me through a bead curtain into a dimly-lit office equipped with a computer, a credit-card machine and a prominent wall safe, hung throughout with signed photographs of grateful clients, including one from the Queen Mum thanking her for a miracle cure to her drinking problem and another from that woman with all the pekinese dogs who writes dirty books, claiming that it had entirely cured her baldness.

I could see that Madame Veronique was casting a beady eye over the contour of my wallet and obediently proffered the cheque in advance for seven hundred nicker plus VAT. On receipt of this the old bird locked it in the wall safe and ushered me into the shower room, where she suggested I should remove all my clothes and step into a marble tub for what she called a freshener. A disembodied voice then instructed me to walk through a second doorway and down

'. . . into a squarish bath containing some lukewarm water . . .'

some steps into a squarish bath containing some lukewarm water. Madame then appeared, this time wearing an oriental wraparound, making mysterious gestures with her hands. The lights changed from blue to pink and from pink to green, and she said I was to lie very still while she passed a current through the bath which would take away all my negative ions. At that moment the telephone rang and I was left alone for ten minutes while she gibbered away to some Duchess and bugger all happened.

A cough reminded her of my presence, and she bustled back in with a little charwoman figure in thick glasses who told me to dry off and lie on a slab, where she slapped a lot of cheap bath oil into the small of my back, humming tunes from the Italian opera.

Quite frankly, Bill, I'd have been better off doing a couple of lengths at the RAC with that old skypilot who was always sitting on the edge with a fag in his mouth chatting up the

6

younger male visitors. I don't know what effect it had on Margaret, but she's been in a pretty grisly mood for the last fortnight. Sailor Ted has now gone absolutely apeshit and froths at the mouth from dawn to dusk, claiming that he invented Europe, that there's a conspiracy to ignore him, write him out of the history books etc. As if that weren't enough Basil Bush flew into Europe for the Brussels do and pulled the rug fairly and squarely from under her. She thought, I suppose understandably, that it was going to be Hopalong all over again, lovey-dovey phone calls all night long, US Pres defers to experienced and statesmanlike British PM. Instead of which Big Baz goes around arm in arm with the Hun, clearly happier knocking back the Schnapps with Old King Kohl than he was being bitten in the back of the neck by the Memsahib. I can't say I blame him.

End result M. comes back to a lot of headlines dictated by Ingham about 'Maggie's Conquest' when in fact she had lost her shirt at the tables, snubbed by Brer Bush who announced that he was now going on a steamer up the Rhine with a German band playing, in preference to a couple of days nagging from M. and being shown round his ancestral home near Epping. I, as you probably saw, was given a walk-on part as the Comic Drunkard gallantly embracing old Grandmaw Bush, who is in fact quite a jolly bird and not averse to a snort, unlike her husband who strikes me as being a long streak of piss.

The only bright spot is the continuing soap opera of the Perils of Pillock. Not only has every lunatic coon in Christendom descended on Vauxhall to screw up his chances in the by-election, but he personally made a prize Charlie of himself on the wireless. A little Scottish Johnnie called McNaughty asked him some perfectly plain question about the interest rates, and Pillock went bananas, tearing the tape out of the machine, and effing and blinding like Prosser-Cluff on a bender. If you ask me the poor fellow's so thick he has to look up his arse to see if he's got his hat on.

See you at Lamberhurst. Your turn to bring the crate I think.

Yours athirst,

DENIS

10 Downing Street
Whitehall

7 JULY 1989

Dear Bill,

I'm sorry I didn't make it to our Wimbledon tryst on Wednesday. The Major picked me up as agreed in his limo and twenty minutes later we had ground to a halt in a motionless jam stretching from Hammersmith to God knows where. It transpired that the Trots and Commies on London Transport and British Rail had downed tools in a desperate attempt to topple the Boss and bring Kinnock to power. In the end we abandoned the Major's limo somewhere in Fulham and spent the rest of the day in a little pub in those parts watching the tennis on the TV.

I gather you were embarrassed by Maurice running amok at the strawberry tent and attempting to strangle the staff on being told the price of a punnet (£14.99). Did you bail him out in the end?

When I got back here the Boss was quivering with rage as she too had been held up in the traffic on her way to some Embassy beano. 'How dare they? How dare they? Strikes are a thing of the past. This is 1989,' she kept on saying after summoning Channon and Fowler and ordering them to outlaw all strikes and threaten Comrade Knapp and his Red Hordes with privatisation unless they came to heel. Channon foolishly pointed out that it was her privatisation plans that had brought them out on strike in the first place and he was duly blasted with her deadly gamma rays and told that the reshuffle could not be long delayed.

Lawson has just been in looking jittery. He was very cocky last week when I saw him putting his empties out and told me to pass on a rude message to Prof. Walters, the boss's American friend on the top floor, to the effect that he could take a long Sabbatical, as the economy was in safe hands. All because his latest monthly statement showed a deficit of a mere £2.5 billion. A couple of days later when all the yuppies had sobered up they decided it wasn't so rosy after all and it was looking as if Mr Nicely might have to jack up the interest rates even higher. Walters was in with the Boss tut-tutting and I-told-you-so-ing but Fatso was unabashed and kept saying: 'Of

8

'. . . *waving a tattered handful of his ill-fated Euro Campaign brochures . . .*'

course Prime Minister, if we had joined the EMS as I myself have always counselled, none of this would have arisen.' Cue for Krakatoa, I need hardly add.

You remember our snuff-taking friend with the bouffant hairdo and the charming smile, Tim 'Tinker' Bell? Alas, I fear his days may be dwindling down to a precious few. Following M's Euro-debacle he was summoned round to the Fuhrer-bunker for a spell in the disorientation room. I saw him having recourse to a pinch of Auld Doctor McJagger's Special Colombian Herbal Mixture before the Boss stormed in, waving a tattered handful of his ill-fated Euro Campaign brochures.

'No wonder we were defeated,' she stormed, 'when this confusing drivel was all our dear people had by way of information. "Stay Indoors if you want Your Helping of Greens!" "Throw a Spanner in the Wogs – Vote Conservative." Who on earth could have approved this childish gibberish? No wonder Mr Heath is emptying the cellars at the Manoir de Quat' Saisons in company with his nautical friends!'

Master Bell crossed and recrossed his legs several times, beaming in an unfocussed manner, and attempting to soothe her. 'Margaret, Margaret, let us not rake over spilt milk! What's done is done. Besides, the campaign was approved at the highest level. You'll see the initials here on the corner of the final draft: "VGMT." '

'Who is this VGMT?' she fumed. 'See to it they are sacked at once, whoever they are, otherwise your friends the Saatchis will be reinstated.'

This caused our friend an outburst of merriment, and he cackled uncontrollably for some moments, blowing his nose with great vigour, and wiping the tears from his cheeks. 'Do you not recognise the delightful handwriting?' he went on, in puckish mood, ' "VG" – Very Good, "MT" – any guesses? Elementary, my dear Denis!' With this he extended his snuff-box to me and seemed quite taken aback when Margaret let out a bull-like roar of rage.

'How can I be expected to see everything that I initial? I am a very busy woman. This is all a plot, isn't it? I see Tebbit's hand in it. Don't laugh, you degenerate! Did Norman dictate this? If you cannot answer, get out! Denis, take Mr Bell by the scruff of the neck and throw him into his Porsche!'

From all this you may gather that nerve-ends are on the tattered side and so it's not surprising that Smellysocks are 14% ahead in the Polls. Howe, incidentally, is beginning to get on her nerves with his muttered hints about the need for a good long rest, re-charging of batteries, he can hold the fort, safe pair of hands etc.

If you ask me he's definitely after her job. It's always those half-asleep johnnies that you've got to watch when it comes to stabbing you in the back. However, with any luck, he may well come a cropper over Hong Kong.

See you at Lamberhurst on the 9th.

Yours unseeded,

DENIS

Dear Bill,

I'm very sorry to hear about Maurice coming unstuck with his Strikebuster Fleet of Army Surplus Three Ton Trucks. I heard another story last night about one of his punters who boarded in Sevenoaks, having paid the £49.99 to the Barbican and back, and ended up in Weston-super-Mare. It transpired that the Muslim Fundamentalist at the wheel, though costing Maurice only a few pence in wages, had arrived in Deal only the night before under a cargo of contraband bananas and dirty books and was not as familiar as he might have been with our road system.

Another lorryload broke down near Blackheath with the engine on fire, and caused a tailback of several miles, leading to a criminal prosecution being brought against Maurice's Board of Directors, i.e. the Major, his lady and that daft girl who they have living upstairs. Much to the Major's chagrin!

None of this has in any way deterred the Boss from embarking on what could, with any luck, be her Last Crusade against the Infidel Unions. Little Walters, the yankee egghead, has had to move out his word processor and all his tartan suitcases so that his room can be transformed into an Operational HQ. Margaret has installed a camp bed, there are maps on the wall showing all the docks, the BR Network, a picture of Mr Scargill and a pair of General Galtieri's bullet-ridden trousers. Here she paces night and day, determined to win the war against the Smellysocks.

'They shall not pass!' I heard her intoning to her War Cabinet as I slipped by the other night to refill my hot water bottle. 'The country is sick to death of these selfish people only interested in money, who do not care a toss about the suffering they cause.' I couldn't help thinking of you and your friends from the Rotary enjoying your regular Wednesday all-day binge at the Station Hotel in Deal, and your frequent toasts, as described to me by the Major, to Mr Knapp and his Merry Men. However Channon, the nearest thing to a Desiree Potato in a suit I have yet to encounter, seemed unaware of this sociological undertow, and had the REME laying miles of steel

11

matting in the Royal Parks to accommodate thousands of determined executives who never alas showed up. 'You're quite right, Prime Minister,' I heard him reiterating, 'I went on one of those big red things with the numbers on the front –' 'Buses,' Margaret prompted in a less than sympathetic tone – 'Yes, and the conditions were absolutely intolerable: some people even had to stand while it was moving along!' 'The important thing, Paul, is that we should be seen to be firm against Socialism. Strikes are a thing of the past. There is no place for them in the Britain of today. No, there is no question of my intervening in the present dispute, but if that duffer Reid gives a penny more than eight percent I have told him that his head will roll!'

'. . . at his first date with Father O'Caravan they both got
paralytic on Madeira . . .'

Talking of rolling heads, I am sorry I couldn't join you and your friend Pringle on your French Revolution Trust House Forte Minibreak to Paris. The graphic re-enactment of Robespierre getting into the bath with Madame Defarge sounded very illuminating for any serious student of history. You probably heard about the Boss's contribution to the Bicentenary when she went on their equivalent of Panorama and told them that the whole thing had been a ghastly waste of time and that Liberte Egalite etc. had all been invented by the British in the days of William and Mary without any of that messy stuff with the Guillotine, in short that there was sod all to celebrate and they should put away their fireworks till the Fifth of November. Mitterand was, predictably, hopping mad like a good Frog, and called her the French equivalent of a daft old bat. This was of course music to Margaret's ears as all she really relishes in life, now she's castrated the Cabinet, is a good scrap with the Euros.

According to the Major, Maurice plans to marry his Maltese Air Hostess lady and is taking instruction with a view to embracing Mother Church. Unfortunately, at his first date with Father O'Caravan they both got paralytic on Madeira while arguing a point of theology and were locked in the vestry by one of the janitors. Maurice smashed a window to get out, and was promptly arrested for breaking in. He's now trying to get his lady friend interested in the C of E.

Yours in the ringside seat,

DENIS

13

10 Downing Street
Whitehall

4 AUGUST 1989

Dear Bill,

I never realised that Mogadon Man had such a big fan club. When you see him, as I do, mooning about in his brothel creepers eyeing the typing pool and pushing his glasses up his nose in a wistful manner, you wouldn't think he would command the undying respect and admiration of people like your dear Daphne and her friends at Drinking for the Disabled.

The Boss has had it in for him for quite a while, ever since he started going round saying he invented Thatcherism and she was merely Miss Piggy, he the man with the hand up the skirt making her eyes go round. After that, whenever they went on those trips abroad things were always pretty frosty away from the arc-lights, and when he started staying out late drinking with all those Belgians it was only a matter of time before the throwing-knife was whistling through the air heading for the spot between his shoulderblades. (I may say that a simultaneous Arrow of God was also hissing through the air bound for fleshier areas between the shoulderblades of Mr Nicely Nicely next door. However, as there was a run on the pound and mass suicides in the City last time she gave him so much as a kick up the arse, it was felt prudent to reprieve him on this occasion. He had, as M. put it, got us into this mess, he could stay on and get us out of it.)

Our scheme, discussed over a few large brownies at Chequers on the Sunday, was to shift the little sod Howe out to Leader of the House along with all the other deadbeats, Channon, Moore etc, and clear the air for the final showdown with Pillock. I remember very clearly writing all this down and Margaret agreeing. My writing may have got a bit illegible towards teatime as I don't remember putting Gummer in at Agriculture, but the main shuffle was clear as a bell.

Our trouble began next morning when friend Howe cut up very rough. M., entre nous, had a bit of a hang-over, was not at her diplomatic best and got caught on the wrong foot by Mogadon's foul language and personal abuse. I've often noticed, Bill, the way in which these amiable old buffers in

14

glasses who you think are a pretty soft option turn out to be very mean-minded, with razor blades sewn in their toecaps when it comes to a scrap. (You remember that chap Pleydell-Bouverie who was briefly on the board at Thatcher Poisonous Paints Division, and the fuss he made when they tried to shift him over to Lubricants?)

Anyway, he obviously smelt a rat as soon as he came in. Margaret suggested Leadership of the House, coupled with a vaguely Whitelaw Elder Statesman role, pottering round pouring oil on troubled waters etc. This was the cue for a Dracula-style transformation from our little friend. Fangs sprouted, bristly hair foamed over his collar, and the eyes behind his spectacles glowed a hideous red. The Boss, as you can imagine, was pretty startled, as she'd never heard language like it since Maurice pranged his motor on our picnic near Hemel Hempstead. Amazed, and in deep shock, she suddenly said, What about the Home Office? 'Aha!' cried the Wolf Man, spinning round, 'does Douglas know his job is up for grabs?' 'Yes,' I heard Margaret falter, 'that is, no – not yet. But I'm sure he would agree to anything I suggest. He always does.' At this, little Howe gave a maniacal laugh, gathered his cloak about him, and swept out in a puff of smoke. I shimmered in later with the Intensive Care on a tray, but the whole thing had clearly left the Old Girl extremely rattled.

The rest of the Living Dead crept in and out during the day, taking their punishment like men. Then at about teatime, with all the reptiles camped out on the pavement snapping at any morsel, the Fiend returned, fortified with advice from his talkative wife, a tough old boot I have often been lumbered with at Christmas rabbiting away in my bad ear: the kind of woman who chews concrete and spits out tintacks. Feeling it my duty to be on hand to protect Margaret if he looked like sinking the fangs in her throat, I hovered by the window as the Mutant put his shiny briefcase on the table and extracted a bulky typescript. 'I may say, Mrs Thatcher, that after your outrageous behaviour this morning my immediate instinct was to resign. However, bearing in mind my solemn duty to our Party and to the country as a whole, I have thought it right to continue. Only, however, if the following demands are met . . .' He then began reading a list which included the Deputy Prime Ministership, poor Fatso's country mansion at Dorney Wood, chairmanship of all Willie Whitelaw's old

'. . . At this, little Howe gave a maniacal laugh, gathered his cloak about him, and swept out in a puff of smoke . . .'

committes, free parking for life and as many Wimbledon tickets as he wanted in perpetuity. If not, he said menacingly, he would tell Hurd that his job had been hawked about only that morning. Margaret pursed her lips, I gave her a nudge suggesting it was a fair cop, and she signed with the blood-filled fountain pen he proffered.

A few very stiff drinks later, we looked at the list and realised that we'd forgotten the Foreign Office, so M. had to ring a little shopwalker figure called Mr Major who not surprisingly couldn't believe his luck and will no doubt continue to embarrass us in the Councils of the Nations for many moons to come. Then, just when we thought the dust had settled the *Daily Telegraph* rang, saying they had had a call from Geoffrey H. denying that Margaret had offered him the Home Office. Had Mr Ingham any comment to make? Hurd was on within seconds, fit to be tied, closely followed by Fatso turning up the hi-fi next door to a volume that cracked the ceiling and thumping on the party wall for the rest of the night calling Margaret a silly old bitch for depriving him of his country seat.

I know they used to say at Burmah that we made a pretty good balls-up of our Board changes, but they hadn't seen anything like this. I've always been superstitious about any hopes of enjoying a well-earned retirement at Dulwich, but I can't help feeling it may at last be on the cards.

Yours over the eight,

DENIS

 10 Downing Street
Whitehall

1 SEPTEMBER 1989

Dear Bill,

I don't think we've corresponded since our misguided Summerbreak in Bonnie Osterreich. Crikey, what a cemetery! I used to think our days with the Widow Glover were pretty good hell on wheels, but Herr Obst, who has a line importing Spode Toby Jugs and represents our economic interests in Vienna, brings a new dimension to holiday torment. He lives in a flat on the slopes of one of those big mountains they have, as featured in *The Sound of Music*. No golf course, and a confirmed tee-totaller. However, knowing my 'little weakness' as he put it, our host very generously supplied me with a bedside miniature of an Alpine liqueur made out of Edelweiss berries. M. had moved in her usual three portakabins full of boxes, secretaries, radio transmitters etc, and spent the whole time on the blower to the UK, buggering up her Ministers' holidays with a lot of gratuitous advice about what they were going to be thinking in the autumn.

I was quite relieved to be back, just in time for the latest

'. . . *very generously supplied me with a bedside miniature of
an Alpine liqueur made out of Edelweiss berries* . . .'

disaster, this time on the Thames. As Margaret opened the
front door, we could hear the special anti-Royal alarm going,
which she had put in at the time of Lockerbie, to give her an
hour's start on the Palace. Only stopping to hand Robin the
Butler her duty-free bags she was out the door again in a flash
and dragging me towards the limo for the motorcade dash to
the River. I don't know if you saw her on the TV, but I
thought she coped with the whole thing very well. Her general
drift was that thanks to her everybody now has a whole lot
more money to spend, with the result that they're all gadding
about on boats and trains and planes leading the life of Riley,
so it's not surprising if from time to time there's the odd
hiccup.

However she was pretty livid, when we were watching the repeat on BBC2, to see that Smarmy Cecil had flown back specially from a 'family holiday' in Florida to muscle in on the act, his face wreathed with concern and spouting a lot of under-rehearsed tosh that sounded to me very much as if it had been put together by Sir Custardface. Within moments she had snatched up her new Mercury Execuphone and was speaking to her erstwhile Mr Cheesecake. 'I just wanted to say, Cecil, how moving I found what you had to say about the poor *Marchioness* victims, but really you shouldn't have bothered to come all the way back from Florida. I was here, surely that was enough?' Matey at the other end must have started in on last year's balls-up when Channon refused to come out of the paddling pool in Mustique when the balloon went up, but the Boss was not convinced. 'No Cecil, we can have too much compassion on these occasions. Why, nice Mr Portillo was coping very well under my direction. I am rather surprised, to tell you the truth, by your lack of judgement. We have to consider each disaster by its merits. Is your hotel room still available in Florida? I think so, yes, Cecil. I'm sure Anne would appreciate having you to herself for a few more precious days.' As you may infer from the above, Bill, the Queen's Favourite may be on his way to the chopping block, i.e. earmarked for the Belfast Job.

Mrs Van der K. has written to invite us both down to the Land of the Free for her pre-election Barbecue and Rottweiler Owners' Lookalike Competition with two days in Sun City thrown in. According to Mr Van der K. who was allowed briefly on the line to give the number of the travel agent, they have a wonderful golf course down there in the middle of a game reserve, or maybe vice versa, so if you chip into the water it's quite likely your caddy will get his leg bitten off going to retrieve it. Mrs Van der K. is I think rightly worried about the way their new leader is moving. It was bad enough when PWB invited Mr Mandela round to tea, but this chap spends his time behaving like Kinnock, having his photograph taken grinning like an elderly chimpanzee in the company of the Frontline Coons. 'If things go on that way,' she writes, 'Horst and I are seriously thinking of transferring our allegiance to the Orange Band of Blood, which is more like your Conservative Party, and also has a charismatic leader who means what he says, like Margaret. His name is Mr Terry Stringemop, also like Margaret an intellectual and a poet.'

Breakfast this morning, I'm sorry to say, was marred by the arrival of another letter from the tall German who owns the *Observer*. I am sending it round to our little friend Mr Farter-Cock with a view to putting him behind bars. It accuses Margaret of being hand in glove with crooks, notably those two very charming Egyptian Johnnies who run Harrods and are always sending us round free calendars.

See you at Maurice's Car Boot Sale at Pevensey Bay. All proceeds to his last Private Clinic, whose final demand ended with a threat to kneecap him.

Yours still transmitting in Outer Space,

DENIS

 10 Downing Street
Whitehall

15 SEPTEMBER 1989

Dear Bill,

I'm sorry to have broken up our little East India and Sports beano the other night when the phone was brought to the table, but once Mrs Van der K. gets on the line there's no stopping her. I entirely understood your leaving shortly after one a.m. and the club servants were putting the chairs on the table by the time I finally induced her to hang up. At that stage, as you probably read in the *Telegraph*, their computerised swingometers down there were predicting a hung parliament, much to Mrs Van der Kaffirbescher's chagrin. 'If anyone is going to be hung, Denis, it should be that little grinning monkey Tutu, for stirring up trouble amongst the Bantu. Even my own houseboy Joshua has taken to handing me Church Literature, which we all know is subsidised from Moscow.' Her views on de Klerk, I need hardly say, were less than complimentary, and PWB was blamed for leaving them in the lurch and 'a prey to the Marxist Jackals and Mongeese of the ANC'. The poor dear had already purchased a new Rottweiler called Kruger, who had that morning bitten the long-suffering Joshua in the fleshy parts, and had got her barbed wire security fence connected to the National Grid. I may say the Boss – 'your good lady' – did not escape the lash of her tongue for hinting that sanctions could not be ruled out indefinitely.

'After all the things she's said to Horst and myself on this very verandah! Why cannot she realise who her true friends are? Why must she go awhoring after that tool of the Kremlin, George Bush?'

Having agreed with much of what she had said up till that point, I had to make vague noises of dissent, whereupon she finally rang off in a rage, calling me a Pinko.

Talking of friend Bush, you may have seen his new autumn self-promotion, codename Crack Down. According to Bell, who knows all about that sort of thing, this was dreamed up by some red spectacle-framed whizzkid on Madison Avenue, and he advised the Boss to buy in on the ground floor. Hence Margaret's sudden concern that British taxpayers' money should be poured into various crooked Colombian fat cats living it up in some godforsaken tropical swamp in the back of beyond that no one until the week before had ever heard of.

The old girl's rather ratty mood was not in any way helped by news of our gallant lager louts throwing themselves and everything else that wasn't screwed to the deck into the briny en route for peace-loving Sweden. The midget Moynihan blew in under the front door within moments for a once-over with the Prime Ministerial steamroller. 'None of this would have happened, Colin, if my ID Cards had been pushed through. These people would all have been arrested before they left home. It is now up to you to blitz these hooligans until they come crawling out with their hands up.' I could see little Moynihan's eyes flickering back towards the front door, obviously in terror lest he might be given the ordeal by empty microphone he got last time, driven out with no warning to announce an extempore twelve-point plan to bring the hooligans to heel. But with the reptiles all off chasing Princess Anne through the rainforest, young Butler had obviously failed to fill the Snakepit in time.

I don't know if you saw Mogadon on the box talking to that Brummy browntonguer – Wheldon? Hogan? – no matter. There was a time when he had the hots for the Boss but that seems to have died down. Anyway, M. was alarmed by what

'. . . codename Crack Down . . . dreamed up by some red
spectacle-framed whizzkid on Madison Avenue . . .'

she read in the public prints, and had the video sent round
to watch before breakfast. What we saw did not improve her
mood. Blinking away behind his fogged glasses, our podgy
erstwhile neighbour came out with a lot of guff about the need
for 'greater Cabinet responsibility', 'more discussion of the
issues', and other euphemisms, all amounting to the suggestion
that Margaret's days were numbered, and that someone with
a more relaxed and bespectacled view of the world would
shortly emerge, Batman-like, dozily to assume the reins of
power.

My own view is that she made a great mistake in heaping him with all those inducements when he dug his heels in last July. Prosser-Cluff would have had his office door walled up before he got back from lunch with a few bits and pieces on the pavement. It's the only language these ambitious little politicos understand.

Did I dream it, or have the Japs bought Wentworth? It wouldn't surprise me, the way things are going. If this turns out to be the case, might it be amusing to hold a Burmah Reunion there, lure Maurice down off the wagon, give him a bottle of brandy and a big box of matches?

Yours, as Vera Lynn put it, till we meet again,

DENIS

 10 Downing Street
Whitehall

29 SEPTEMBER 1989

Dear Bill,

Crikey, what a triumph! I don't know whether you were still conscious at the end, but I think the Major and I lost you in the Glenfiddich tent. My eyes were blinded with tears when Jacklin accepted the trophy. Anyway, on the way to the car-park Maurice spotted a group of woebegone old Americans in tartan jackets, ran up to them, and threw all their hats into the Johnny Walker Canal Hazard. The Major and I had to restrain him when the Constabulary showed up, and they led him away for conspiring to cause a disturbance. I explained to Houghton Mifflin III, the leader of the little party, that our friend had a problem with alcohol abuse, and he was most understanding, inviting us all back for a snort at the Sutton Coldfield Ramada, where he had a suite. Mrs Mifflin, quite a big woman, turned out to be an ex-stripper, and was, I think, persuaded later on in the evening to take a trip down memory lane. But Mr Mifflin's Tequila Preemptive Strikes were very powerful and I'm told I collapsed shortly before the floor show.

'. . . Mrs Mifflin . . . turned out to be an ex-stripper, and was, I think, persuaded later on in the evening to take a trip down memory lane . . .'

I was at any rate pretty shattered to be awoken a few hours later by a person-to-person call from the Boss in Japan. How she knew where I was I have no idea, but I blame Boris. She said it was the middle of the afternoon there, and she had just come from a fascinating lunch at which she'd given the Nips a jolly good talking-to about stopping our Fortnum & Mason hampers reaching their supermarkets. Had I remembered to double-lock the back door at Number Ten? Had I eaten up the remains of the Lymeswold quiche in the upstairs fridge? I was about to explain that it was the middle of the night in Sutton Coldfield when a Japanese voice interrupted to say: 'The party you are speaking to is not available repeat not available at present. Kindly call again later.' After this the line went dead, and so did I.

When I got back to Downing Street, in pretty bad shape, I accused Boris of leaking my whereabouts. He said it was probably MI5, who he thinks are trying to destabilise the Boss for making them go public, and even suspects them of including little Gummer in the Cabinet List when neither of us can remember mentioning him. He said the Mem had now hit Moscow; he'd seen her on his MoskwaTV Link doing a party political for Gorbo, telling the Russians that they'd never had it so good and that the day of freedom was dawning when they would be able to buy Fortnum & Mason hampers in their GUM department store. According to Boris, there had been a renewed request from Gorbo for a Royal Visit from HM the Q, but the Boss said it would be quite inappropriate and that Russian consumers would be confused to see another woman arrive when they had grown used to the idea of herself as supreme leader.

When she finally got back she was fit to be tied, as the D of E had pulled a fast one by getting front page coverage with the latest IRA beastliness in Deal. Poor little Bell! They were in Moscow when they got the news and he immediately hired a helicopter to whisk her across the border to Finland, with a private BMW Vertical Take Off Fanjet kindly lent by Richard Branson standing by on the runway ready to speed her to Gatwick, where a second Silver King Minicopter had its engines ticking over ready for the dash to Deal. All went according to plan until the Customs at Gatwick, working on a tip-off from Colombia, decided to take the helicopter apart. It was while she was twiddling her thumbs in the VIP lounge waiting for a limo that she saw the headline in the paper saying the Duke had beaten her to it by six hours.

Since then the air here at Number Ten has been blue with invective and a formal protest has been biked round to Buckingham Palace. 'Who does he think he is? It is entirely unconstitutional for members of the Royal Household to comment on these sensitive issues!' She was even angrier when the Smellysocks started making capital out of the fact that she had farmed out the Guardhouse at Deal to a 'more competitive' firm of security consultants run by Help the Aged.

I've just had Maurice's Miss Mifsud, formerly of Air Malta, on the line in tears to say that Maurice had upped sticks and left her for a harpy in the Green party. According to her barely coherent account, the woman used to be a big noise in the

National Front and then retired to run a health food shop in Abbots Langley. Maurice met her on an Intercity to Birmingham, and they've now been photographed 'attuning' together before the Greens' Conference. Miss Mifsud had been finding literature in his pockets for some days about the Green Way to Intoxication, which involves boiling nettle leaves with deadly nightshade and inhaling it from a bronchitis kettle. He is now going to stand as a delegate, if he can.

Plans for the Conference follow, marked Top Secret.

Au reservoir a Effingham.

Your old Evening Primrose,

DENIS

B L A C K P O O L

13 OCTOBER 1989

Dear Bill,
I can't say I blame you for declining to visit me in this hell-hole. There are the usual Colditz-style security regulations in force and you can't even go to the Gents without having to prove your identity to a woman from the Gestapo. It's all completely out of hand. I don't know if you saw but the latest thing is that they are going to put up iron railings at the bottom of Downing Street to keep out the Provos. I said what about bona fide travellers trying to get in after important board meetings at the Club and wasn't it a bit much, at my time of life, to have to risk life and limb clambering over spiky railings in the middle of the night? Boris says we're all going to be issued with electronic passes which are supposed to open the gates. (Which reminds me, you probably heard that Maurice got stuck in one of those new-fangled barriers on the underground and they had to get the fire brigade to extract the old boy.)

There was the usual pre-conference flap on, particularly since Tinker Bell, having watched the Smellysocks' equivalent at Brighton, decided that Pillock was finally getting his product across and was beginning to establish consumer credibility with the A-B's (i.e. they'd all put on suits and ties to look like Smarmy Cecil). Anyway, the Boss is under pressure to come off with a cracker of a speech and knock Ginger Nuts for six, but with Sir Custardface still on the payroll, I can't see this happening (his latest [rejected] joke: 'Well, they may have got rid of Red Ken, but when are they going to get rid of Red Kin? [i.e. Pillock]'). The old boy was sitting in my den puffing away at his cigarette holder and desperately leafing through the Nigel Rees Joke-Book for After Dinner Speakers when we heard a bit of a commotion downstairs with the Boss's voice raised in anger. I tiptoed down to find that Matey from next door had breezed in to announce the jacking up of interest rates to 15%. 'You yourself, Prime Minister, have stressed on many occasions,' he was saying, 'that we should not shrink from unpopular measures, whatever the circumstances and whilst I appreciate that the Party conference is upon us . . .' 'Fiddlesticks,' cried the Boss, switching on the Exterminate and Destroy Rays, 'you have done this quite deliberately at this time in order to promote a crisis. I know who is behind this, you and your friend Howe. I knew I should never have given in to his demands.' 'Come, come,' soothed our obese neighbour, lifting a podgy hand, 'let us not give way to unseemly hysteria, Prime Minister, we must do everything, as you yourself have often so rightly stressed, to keep inflation up – I mean down.' This rather spoilt the effect of his little speech and the Boss launched a further dose of the deadly rays, threatening him with the usual routine, i.e. a stiff talking-to from Professor Walters followed by replacement by Smarmy C.

The long and the short of it was that they had to sit up all night re-drafting the Boss's speech in a more Churchillian vein including, I may say, most of Lawson's guff about never having shirked unpopular measures in the interests of short-term political gain, etc, etc.

However, as I reminded her later, these interest rates are only bad news for the foolish virgins who have borrowed a lot of money from the building societies. Wise chaps like you and I will be laughing all the way to our deposit accounts. But we won't say this in the speech.

*'. . . the Boss has been sticking pins into the wax model of
Runcie . . .'*

I need hardly say that since his visit to Rome the Boss has
been sticking pins into the wax model of Runcie. Not content
with farting round the Vatican curtseying to the Pope, he gave
an interview to the Eyetie media accusing the Boss of being
a Sadducee passing by on the other side. Quite obviously, he
has failed to read, mark and inwardly digest the Gospel of St
Margaret as preached by the Blessed Tebbit. Munster, you
may remember, very sensibly pointed out some time back that
the Good Samaritan was a fully paid up member of the Conservative Party with a healthy balance at the NatWest and was
thus in a position to help the less fortunate. Now that Runcie's
plan to hand over the C of E to the Pope has fallen flat, the

Boss is going to suggest that he hands over control to her friend the Chief Rabbi, a fierce little bearded johnny who is very sound on all the important things like cracking down on the arsebandits. I said the Chief Rabbi's first task should be to boot out all the black sheep, Runcie, Durham & Co, and bring in some sound chaps in the Archie Wellbeloved mould.

Smarmy Cecil has just glimmered in with his plans to nationalise British Rail. You'd think they'd got enough on their hands with the water balls-up, but apparently he's planning a big speech for this week with details of the carve-up. I know Maurice has written to him with an early bid for Network South East.

Must dash. Boss has organised outing of Rowdies to go and break up Tarzan's Fringe meeting in the Amusement Arcade.

Those about to die salute you,

DENIS

 10 Downing Street
Whitehall

27 OCTOBER 1989

Dear Bill,

You say I sounded raving mad on the blower from K.L. As I'd spent the whole afternoon playing golf with Lee Kuan Yew and a couple of Top Coons' relations who didn't know a niblick from a trombone in a temperature of 110° in the shade, it may be that my nerve-ends were a little frayed. I may say I also paid a courtesy visit to the relict of the late Prosser-Cluff. You may remember her, a native lady who ran the Golden Horseshoe in Princess Alexandra Crescent. (Happy days, what?) She is now very frail, but spoke of the old boy with impressive acrimony recalling the time he set fire to the Coolies' dwellings when they asked for one per cent across the board.

As you can imagine, it was no great sacrifice to tear myself away from the Great Durbah. I didn't mind it so much in the

'. . . I suggested a quick one after the opening speeches and he looked at me as if I was trying to sell him my grandmother . . .'

old days when Mogadon was on the strength, as he was never averse to slipping behind the curtain for the odd treble in the shade of the Koolibar Tree. This new chap they've got, however, Major, is made of more tedious stuff. I suggested a quick one after the opening speeches and he looked at me as if I was trying to sell him my grandmother. 'Mrs Thatcher, I'm sure, would not approve. Besides, I have agreed to be behind her on the platform at all times, ready to be told what to say when my turn comes.' Before I could reply, the Boss beckoned him over, his features were transformed into an oily smile, and with a cry of 'Coming, Prime Minister!' he positively slid across the floor like that brown-tongued Greek waiter at the RAC, the one Maurice threw a pancake at.

The Boss became more and more brassed off as the week unfolded, her mood having been in no way brightened by her treatment at the hands of the Windsor woman on board *Britannia*. First of all, the D of E fitted a tripwire for her on the gangplank, and could be seen roaring with laughter amidships as M. measured her length on the duckboarding. Then they switched the placecards so that she had to spend the whole of dinner listening to Eebagum on one side lecturing her on the evils of apartheid and that skinny Socialist streak of piss Bob Hawke regaling her with earthy Australian jokes on the other. My own evening passed in something of a blur, sitting next to Mrs Currie and wondering what she was doing there. Afterwards I was told it was Mrs Bhutto and that my affecting to discover Salmonella in the Lobster Bisque had gone down like a lead balloon.

Come Sticky Time HM the Q staggered to her feet to propose her own health, massed bands played the anthem, and then to everyone's surprise she launched into an unscheduled cabaret act in which she likened the gathering to 'one big family party', drawn together by mutual bonds and a common parentage, a family in which inevitably there were sometimes tensions, caused by the presence – and at this point she shot Margaret a fishy look over her bifocals – of an awkward old aunt who refused to join in the fun and wanted to have everything her own way.

I could tell from the slam of drawers and the banging of cupboards in the next room that this had not been taken in good part by the Mem, and when Major tapped on my door a few moments later to say he had been rung for I surmised that some retaliation was afoot. Her revenge was not long in coming. Having put her monicker to the form of words threatening Mr de Klerk with all manner of evil should he fail to come to heel, she summoned the reptiles to a last-minute briefing. De Klerk, she told them, was a thoroughly decent bloke who deserved a pat on the back for allowing the Darkies into the swimming pools, and had frequently entertained enterprising British businessmen, including in point of fact the Boy Mark, with a view to furthering trade between our two countries. Even little Major looked a bit green round the gills as the hacks raced away to their telephones after a week of inertia, and the Happy Family Group, at that moment assembling on the lawn for a snapshot round the Great White Mother, immediately broke up with shouts and snarls.

I rang Mrs Van der K. later on to say how well Margaret

had done on her behalf, and got a bit of an earful. Apparently de Klerk had invited Tutu over to tea and released a lot of elderly terrorists. 'Mark my words, Denis, they will be letting the animals out of the zoos at this rate. I don't know why de Klerk doesn't just hand them a machine gun and blindfold himself. This is all your Margaret's fault for hobnobbing with the Frontline Jackals. You cannot play poker with the tar babies without staining your nice clean trousers.'

When we got home Professor Walters, our American p-g with the tartan suitcases, was cockahoop. He made us both very large Martinis, and brought us a selection of press cuttings in which he figured putting the boot into Matey Next Door, whom he described as 'an overweight buffoon'. 'Isn't this great, Prime Minister? It worked just a treat.' 'What do you mean, Professor?' M. asked in a dangerously low tone. 'This is going to cause me a great deal of trouble. There might even be another run on the pound. People will lose confidence in us.' 'But I only did what you said, Chief. Little piece in the *Cincinnati Financial Weekly*. Your Mr Bell gets it faxed into every newspaper in Great Britain and Shazaam, Fatso is in deep doodoo.'

Nor was Margaret overjoyed by Greaser Hurd releasing waves of Bogtrotters into the community. I was fortunate enough to be tucked away out of sight behind the *Sporting Life* when he shuffled in for his carpeting. 'We cannot have this, Douglas. People will laugh every time 'a judge opens his mouth. Our prisons will be emptied within weeks. I've already had little Mr Haughey on the line this morning saying some people in Birmingham should be let out as well.' Hurd began to splutter in the usual way, saying we had to play the game. 'Exactly, Mr Hurd, and they must not win, they must not win. We showed the way at Gibraltar, and now look what you're doing!' (If only M. would reintroduce the death sentence, as I've always argued, none of this would have happened.)

Yours wallowing in a bottle of best Scotch,

DENIS

10 Downing Street
Whitehall

10 NOVEMBER 1989

Dear Bill,

Thank you so much for writing all those individually signed letters to backers of the infamous High Speed Link, warning them that they would get their fingers very badly burned should they proceed. It seems to have done the trick. I talked to young Mr Ferrett of Ferrett, Ferrett and Shine, our Estate Agents in Dulwich, and he told me that prices have definitely bottomed out and with this latest climb down by BR are now on the upturn. I went in the other morning to take off the plastic sheeting and check the thermostat in the Win-O-Store with a view to being in by Christmas, and everything seemed to be holding up very well considering it's a new building. Signs of mice in M's en suite kitchenette off the master bedroom, but otherwise hunky-dory.

The only snag, and it's a big one, is whether the Boss can be persuaded to see sense and get out before they blow her out. As things stand she is subject to very violent changes of mood, rather reminiscent of Squiffy's better half when they had to fly her back from Miami in a special plane on BUPA.

If you saw her on the box with that little Walden fellow you probably formed your own medical opinion. One moment Bette Davis, the next the She-Beast from Thirty Thousand Fathoms.

What little Walden, very unwisely in my view, kept needling away at was her 'relationship' with our old p-g, Professor Walters, the one with the tartan suitcases. Lawson would have stayed if she'd sacked the Professor, why hadn't she done so? Instead of coming clean and saying she wanted nothing more than to see the back of our obese neighbour, she went on and on about how she couldn't understand why Porky had resigned and how she'd knelt repeatedly on the carpet, clinging to the back flap of his jacket and pleading with him to remain.

What she didn't realise was that Fatso was billed in the same slot the week after, and had clearly briefed the Brummy Sparrow to provoke her into saying exactly this. He could then shimmer in the following Sunday and accuse her of being a liar. With some justification, alas. I was unfortunately privy

'. . . she'd knelt repeatedly on the carpet, clinging to the back flap of his jacket . . .'

to their historic leave-taking on the stairs at Number Ten, having dozed off on the settee in Boris's staff rest-room. I was woken just before lunch by a voice raised in anger, which I instantly recognised as that of our gourmet ex-Chancellor. 'Very well, if he's only an adviser, as you keep on saying, why don't you give him the push?' 'Advisers advise,' I heard the shrill tones of my spouse repeating her now familiar mantra. 'Advisers advise and will continue to do so!' 'If you ask me,' Fatso roared back, 'that Yankee streak of piss has been doing a good deal more than advising you. Advise and consent, more like! Why did he need all those suitcases?' 'How dare you?' my wife replied. 'Advisers advise, they can do no more!' 'Everything I've said about the EMS, you two pump out leaks contradicting it, trying to undermine me. Well, I've had it up to here. I'm going!' 'Just because you're too cowardly to clear up all the mess you've been making! What was it St Francis of Assisi said? "No man having put his foot in the plough can take it out again!" That is a lesson you have still not learned, Nigel!' 'Oh sod off!' With this the front door slammed, and I could hear the Boss snapping off banisters in her fury.

In the circs I thought it best to lie doggo with a bottle or two of Boris's Buffalo Grass Vodka. When I came round the Boss was clearly back on a high. 'There you are, Denis! Well, that's all settled. We are well rid of him. John Major has been aching to take the controls, Douglas has dreamed of the FO since he was in short trousers, I can't remember who we've got at the Home Office, but I'm told he's a safe pair of hands. It is time to close ranks and turn victory into defeat. I mean the other way round.'

There then followed a lull of some hours during which M. retired to her den to work on her anti-European strategy, and I felt it was safe to turn on the TV for the sports news. There, to my dismay, was the Dead Sheep from Outer Space, Mr Mogadon, being quizzed by the world's media. M. entered the room just as he began to push his glasses up his nose and reiterate his faith in the European Idea. 'Traitor! I might have known it!' the Boss growled, snatching up the telephone to Ingham. 'Why was this not cleared with me?' There was a longish pause as she listened to Ingham's faltering reply. 'So. Hurd was in it as well. And Major. The ingratitude, after all I have done for them! Is there no one I can trust? Men!!'

I thought it advisable to toddle downstairs at this juncture to see if the second post had come, when a brand new Porsche drew up and who should emerge but the somewhat dishevelled figure of smarmy Cecil. 'Denis, you bastard!' he cried, propelling me into a corner of the hall and talking in a husky conspiratorial tone. 'What was your share-peddling friend called? Picarda? You told me he was squeaky clean! Now the Trots have rumbled me. I'm ruined. Where is she?' I tried to persuade him that the Boss probably had enough on her plate without that kind of news, but he said he had to go through with it, stroked his Brylcreemed hair back, composed his face into a brave smile and began to drag himself up the stairs. Within seconds the smoke alarm had gone into operation and he was back in the hall, a crumpled and broken man. If it was a case of reptiles out for his blood, I counselled, why not get in touch with the Major's funny little lawyer friend Friar-Tuck? Or was it Smelter-Ratt? In any event the one I got in to fire a shot across the bows of the tall German who owns the *Observer*. He promised to take my advice, though why I should do anything to help the little greaser God alone knows, and slunk out through the doomed portal.

Could you get on to Maurice's Gentle Gorilla Removal firm to see if they might ferry our kit down to Dulwich at fairly short notice?

See you at the Cenotaph.

Yours at the going down of the sun,

DENIS

 10 Downing Street
Whitehall

24 NOVEMBER 1989

Dear Bill,

Sorry you couldn't make it to the Halitosis Open Day on Tuesday. Not that you missed much. I only stayed long enough to see the Boss walking up the aisle with Pillock, which always makes me laugh. Having had a good snigger behind my hand, I managed to extricate myself from among the other distinguished strangers – the usual sweaty crush of coon emissaries – and sloped off to Annie's Bar as soon as HM put her specs on to read out the Boss's essay on What I Am Going To Do This Term.

Blow me, who should I find occupying the whole length of the bar but our erstwhile neighbour Fatty Lawson, cradling an enormous brownie and in expansive mood. 'Ah, Denis, you old piss-artist, couldn't face your little woman's pearls of wisdom, what? Can't say I blame you! The usual? A bucket of Gordon's for the gentleman, Doris, and go easy on the tonic!'

He told me I wouldn't believe what a relief it was not having to talk to 'that ghastly old bat' any more. The sense of silence. Did I know what it was like, when the dentist gave you the pink water to drink and told you to rinse out, he'd see you in a fortnight when the bleeding had stopped? You know me,

'. . . I only stayed long enough to see the Boss walking up the aisle with Pillock . . .'

Bill; never one to look a free snort in the mouth, and I mumbled something about the Boss being a very remarkable woman.

At this our fat ex-Chancellor slapped me very hard on the back, gave a roar of laughter, and addressing the various no-hopers slumped at nearby tables, exclaimed: 'Poor old Foureyes! Hear what he said? "Very remarkable woman!" That's pretty rich, I must say!' One particularly cherry-nosed old party – officially one of ours – thereupon blew his nose and said he'd always admired Margaret, but why didn't I have a word in her ear, she wouldn't listen to any of *them*, God knows they'd tried, and tell her Christmas was coming up, she'd done a marvellous job and so forth, why didn't she get out while she was ahead.

I don't think you'll consider I was disloyal, Bill, if I tell you I said I was very much in favour. Cut a long story short, I bought a few rounds, and we persuaded that very gloomy Old Etonian, Cemeteryface Gilmour, to do his duty for Queen and Country and put himself up for the Leadership. Lawson fell on the floor laughing, but we all agreed it was a jolly good idea. I think Gilmour had had a few, and after a bit of mock modesty he said okay. Then he came back from the gents looking a bit worried. When he'd found his glass again we asked him what the trouble was. Bit of a snag; what if he won? At this there was more laughter, Lawson ordered quadruples all round, and Cemeteryface, still looking very gloomy, was persuaded to sign his name in blood.

I had a bit of a turn myself the other night. I'd been out to dinner with some East German businessman friend of Boris's and may have overimbibed, but for the life of me I couldn't get my latchkey into the keyhole at Number Ten. After a certain amount of scratching about the door was opened, and a little man with glasses came out and asked if he could help. For some reason I was convinced it was the man who comes round every week to spray disinfectant into the telephones. I was rather surprised to find him there in the middle of the night, and even more so when he offered me a drink.

Do you know, Bill, it got odder and odder. Hardly had he put a tumbler of Alka-Seltzer in my hand when a little woman bounced in in a frilly dressing gown and pom-pom slippers crying: 'Do come upstairs, darling, I've hung the Green Lady over the mantelpiece in our bedroom and she looks really classy!' At this the Phonotas gent cleared his throat, straightened his specs, and said: 'Darling, may I introduce our next-door neighbour, Mr Thatcher.' In a flash all was revealed.

Boss had a pretty grisly weekend with the Euros, trying to put them straight on the Rolling Back of the Curtain. Her line was why, when intelligent Europeans beyond the Pale are throwing off the shackles of bureaucracy, should we be busily locking them on? Good deal of grave head-shaking from the assembled Euros who began to speak with tongues, trying to make Margaret feel she was some kind of idiot housewife with a shopping bag who had wandered in uninvited.

In answer to your enquiry about the Boy Mark, I am glad to say I have not seen him. I gather he flew in to London a week or so ago, and is staying at the Holiday Inn with a black butler called Otis and a large entourage of masseurs and accountants. Why old Beefburger puts up with it I can't imagine.

Yours at Twilight,

DENIS

10 Downing Street
Whitehall

8 DECEMBER 1989

Dear Bill,

Thank you for your commiserations. I'd rather given up hope of Sir Anthony Meyer romping home with an overall majority even before they went to the urns, but it was still very disappointing. Cemeteryface behaved quite disgracefully. Having as I told you put his monicker to the deed in human gore over a few large ones in Annie's Bar, he came to us baggy under the eyes the following morning and said that Meyer was making such a good show of it he felt it would be ungentlemanly for him to take over the baton on the last lap. What a creep.

God knows, we tried. Meyer popped up out of the blue and appeared on the TV walking his wife and his dog on the common, and playing the part of the decent old gent, reluctantly quitting the plough to challenge the evil Grocer's Daughter who has cast a blight on the fair land of Avalon. I immediately got on the blower pledging my support. Bell & Co got the wind up good and proper and had the Chief Whip down the greasy pole with all alarm bells ringing. Little Renton, poor soul, was to be sent round to all the MPs to issue threats of GBH if they stepped out of line, and Margaret was to be launched on a wall-to-wall media hype using her New Formula Softer-Than-Soft Goes Right Round the Bend.

Tinker therefore got on to the BBC, telling them that

Margaret might graciously condescend to manifest herself on Panorama, on the condition that Dimbleby confined himself to no more than two questions and made no reference to the Economy. This went ahead as planned, but unfortunately the Boss lost her cool in the first round and used the old gouge and butt tactics on the Bouffant Lothario of the small screen, causing a good deal of wincing and pallor on the part of Bell and his team as they watched it in the Ops Room.

Meanwhile, according to Boris, the Dirty Tricks Squad had been out in force, combing the newspaper library at Colindale for any filth on the silver-haired Challenger from the Shires. After thousands of hours poring over the microfilm, they discovered that he'd once been in the FO, and the next day one of the Blatts ran an obedient piece about him being chased through Moscow by a mentally deficient prostitute on her bicycle. MI5 came round in force with their Autumn Smear Catalogue, their latest line you might be amused to hear being that Heseltine didn't really resign over Westland but was caught dressed up in Nazi uniform strangling rabbits for pleasure in a sauna in Hemel Hempstead. When you read it in the *Sun* remember you got it first from yours truly.

The only visible result of all this activity was to produce the small wave of sympathy for Sir Anthony discernible in the poll.

I'm sorry I couldn't come out on Sunday, we had to give lunch to that chap with the funny moustache from Danzig. The Boss was initially very over the moon to hear of his arrival. 'You see, Denis, they know me as their liberator. It is because of what we have achieved in this country that the people of Eastern Europe have been inspired to throw off the shackles of state control and Trade Union monopoly power.' When I pointed out that Brian Redbeard on the BBC had said Mutton-chops was over at the invitation of Ron Todd and his Merry Men I could see I had spoken out of place, and poor old Walensky got the most tremendous bollocking over the coffee and petits fours about our unions not being like unions on their side. The next time he came, he would have to get in touch with Central Office who would 'arrange his trip' together with suitable expenses.

What wonderful news about your friend Toby Aldington being exonerated for War Crimes. As you said in your very moving letter, which of us who slogged it in the 39–45 show

40

'. . . one of the Blatts ran an obedient piece about him being chased through Moscow by a mentally deficient prostitute on her bicycle . . .'

can put his hand on his heart and say he wasn't involved in distastefulness of one kind or another? Maurice, I know, has been having to drink very heavily for fear of sleepless nights at the thought of his business activities in Port Said being dragged up all over again. As the Judge said, surely it is time that these things were finally given a decent burial. As for people comparing Toby's disagreeable duties to what's going on now with the Boat People, my opinion is that the little yellow folk have only themselves to blame. They could easily have seen in the *Telegraph* what conditions were like in Hong Kong before they bought their one-way tickets on the black market, and in any case, according to a man I met at the Club, they get a very warm reception on their return, with free shopping vouchers and a signed photograph of Ho Chi Minh.

Boss is just off to Strasbourg for another punishing twenty rounds with the Eurocommies. Zut Alors blew into London for a photocall as part of Bell's campaign to remodel Margaret's more bending image, and a filthier four-letter fellow I have yet to clap eyes on.

Are you coming to Maurice's Christmas Party? He had a bit of a windfall when Young asked him to mastermind the Rover deal and has, he tells me, invested it in some very good Albanian vodka. We could combine it with a shopping spree at Lillywhite's.

Yours at the check-out,

DENIS

10 Downing Street
Whitehall

22 DECEMBER 1989

Dear Bill,

I'm afraid our envisaged Boxing Day scenario is going to have to go to the wall. In the spirit of Mother Teresa, the Boss has invited the sick, the halt and the lame, to wit the Majors, the Waddingtons and the Gummers. Not much festive spirit there, you will opine, and you would be right, but it's a seventeen-line whip as somebody has to wear the paper hat and clown about for them. To complete our Yuletide bliss, our born-again friend Brother Rupert Murdoch sent down a free satellite dish to Chequers, in case we should miss Derek Jameson's Bundle of Yo Ho Ho Christmas Culture. Mr Wu rang late last night in a bit of a state, saying he'd been picketed by the local branch of the CPRE, Mrs Mortimer-Heseltine and her friend Lady Starborgling, who were complaining about his having erected the dish in a manner likely to detract from the historic character of a Listed Building. Apparently they'd stood there until he'd taken it down and then smashed it with their umbrellas. God works, as little Runcie often observes, in a very mysterious way.

Have you seen the Boss on Halitosis TV at all? I find it hard

*'. . . Mr Wu rang late last night in a bit of a state, saying
he'd been picketed by the local branch of the CPRE . . .'*

to recognise her – all sweetness and light, butter wouldn't
melt in her mouth. Little Pillock doesn't know whether he's
coming or going. He comes bouncing into the ring, all geared
up for twenty punishing rounds with the Iron Lady, only to
be enveloped in a cloud of Je Reviens and motherly affection.
This is all the work of our bouffant-haired friend Mr Bell, who
as soon as the idea of TV cameras in the Hall looked like getting past M's stalwart opposition sent for that little greaser who
used to do the Juke Box Jury, David Jacobs, to come round
and coach her in his famous Brown Voice Technique. From
the altercations I heard emanating from the Den this clearly
took a bit of doing. The first couple of lessons ended in tears,
with poor Jacobs sobbing on my shoulder saying he hadn't

heard language like that since the days of Sir Gerald Nabarro on Any Questions. I eventually took matters into my own hands and invited the obsequious Master of Ceremonies into Boris's Christmas Grotto for one of my Glasnost Megasnorts. He sprang through the door like a tiger unleashed, and sure enough within moments I could hear the Boss cooing like an Undertaker's Mute, 'Will the Right Honourable Gentleman, with the greatest possible respect, I know he may find it very hard to understand this, have a little care and compassion for those who will inevitably, through no fault of their own . . .' while little Jacobs hopped up and down, clapping her impersonation of him like that head waiter when Maurice balanced a brandy glass on the late Mrs Waddilove's nose.

This new Softer than Soft tone is, I need hardly say, only for TV consumption. You should have heard her on the telephone to poor Hurd over the Pope and the Boat People. 'How dare he interfere in our affairs, sitting there in his luxury palazzo? How many of these people has he offered to accommodate in the Vatican, I should like to know?' I could hear the wretched Hurd doing his strong oil on troubled waters bit in the best FO manner, but he might just as well have saved his breath. 'How did these international meddlers and busybodies come to hear about this at all? Because of your bungling incompetence! You old Etonians are all the same, smug, supercilious and lacking in any kind of guts! Don't interrupt me, Douglas, I knew it was a mistake to move Major. He would not have allowed this whole messy business to explode in this way. No wonder all my MPs are up in arms. What on earth could you have been thinking of, throwing open the floodgates to so many Chinamen? How dare you suggest it was my idea! I am arranging for a microphone to be put up on the pavement outside Number Ten. If you are not standing behind it with a good explanation in three minutes I shall reluctantly assume that you have resigned. I know dear David Waddington will be very happy to add your Portfolio to his own.'

I don't know whether you've glimpsed this Waddington bird on your travels. 'Is he one of us?' I hear you cry. I'm not altogether sure. Initially I rather warmed to him when I heard he believed in the gallows as a means of restoring sanity to public life, but on closer acquaintance I think he may be a bit too shell-shocked to have any very clear opinions about anything, rather like that friend of Prosser-Cluff's who used to have his gloves attached to his overcoat with bits of elastic. Margaret, I think, sees him in the same category as our little friend next door, i.e. living proof that the so-called Offices of State can function perfectly well with a dummy in the chair.

Talking of Glasnost, the spirit of Gorby has begun to affect even the Smellysocks and word is they're thinking of changing the name of the Labour Party to the Conservative and Unionist Party. Officially in order to line up behind Zut Alors, they have come out strongly against the Union Closed Shop. Next thing we'll hear, no doubt, is that squads of demonstrators have broken into Ron Todd's bungalow and unearthed a cache of US Defense Bonds and inflatable rubber women.

Enclosed is something I brought back from Johannesburg earlier in the year. Apply a lighted cigarette to Mr Mandela's hind-quarters and I think you'll be amused.

May Yuletide Fun illuminate
Dear Friend, both you and yours
Don't drive if you're inebriate
Or crawling on all fours.
(Issued by the Home Office)
Yours doggo,

DENIS

 10 Downing Street
Whitehall
5 JANUARY 1990

Dear Bill,
Oh dear, oh dear. DT in doghouse yet again. As you probably know, the Mem is by way of having a little Durbah for the deserving poor on Boxing Day, with all kinds of waifs and strays like the unemployed dramatist Sir Custardface being invited in from the hedgerows for a mulled Ribena and a Tesco mince pie. In the midst of these festivities I trotted to the door for a breath of Highland Mist and found a little man in specs trying to park his Metro in the sweep. Somewhat the worse for wear, I must confess, I thumped on his roof and told him in no uncertain terms that the likes of Phonotas used the

45

Tradesman's Entrance, and that he should report to Mr Wu forthwith. Little fellow very obedient, and I thought no more of it.

Bugger me, five minutes later, Wu comes chortling into the throng wearing his green apron, followed by aforesaid four-eyes plus overdressed spouse. 'Mr Denis, he makee Number One Ballsup, Your Highness. This man he no phonewasher, ha, ha, Ladies and Gentlemen, he Chancellor of Exchequer. Mr Denis he dlunk. Too much lookee at electlic soup. Ha ha.' By this time Margaret's expression had turned to thunder, and Mr Wu was left to enjoy his joke alone.

Later on she had the TV wheeled in so we could watch the Boxing Day atrocities from Romania, and thawed sufficiently to tap on her glass and make a short speech. How wonderful it was that her ideas had fallen on such fertile soil throughout Eastern Europe, and that bastion after bastion of Marxist-Leninism was crumbling before all-conquering Thatcherism. 'Let us raise our glasses, ladies and gentlemen. I give you the toast "To Freedom!"' There was a good deal of thumping on the table at this, Cecil P. burst into tears, and Jeffrey Archer stood on a chair and began to sing 'Rule Britannia'. Just then, little Howe, who had been refilling his glass surreptitiously from a stone bottle under the table, staggered to his feet, spectacles skew-whiff, and signalled for silence. 'Dear friends, I am sure the Prime Minstrel would like me to thank you all for joining us on this hysterical occasion. The tyrant is over-thrown. We see today that dictators, of whatever colour or sex . . .' I could see the Boss beginning to fume, and signalling to Wu to remove the bottle. '. . . eventually come unstuck, they are toppled. Bang bang bang. They are replaced by men of moderation and indecency. Gentlemen, the Queen!' At this he fell out of sight, much to the chagrin of Elspeth, his talkative wife, who emptied a jug of water over his head and began to prod him with her umbrella.

I don't have any very clear recollection of what followed, but fairly late on I was having a snooze behind the Christmas tree when I was collared by our bouffant-haired image-maker, Tinker Bell, looking v. down in the mouth. He'd just come back from Chile, where he had been masterminding the election campaign of some would-be dictator who had plans to take over from our old chum Buffy Pinochet. Alas, the Chileans had not bought Bell's pitch, and his man had limped in

'. . . *Jeffrey Archer stood on a chair and began to sing "Rule Britannia". . .*'

without his deposit. Bell described leaving the country in a hail of gunfire and not a sniff of his bill being paid. I refilled his beaker, but he became increasingly maudlin. Every product had its natural shelf-life, he confessed. There was a limit to the amount of new packaging anybody could do. In the end the punters would always fall for some new brand. I eventually twigged he was talking about my little woman – even if he was comparing her to some kind of detergent. I found myself becoming increasingly buoyant at the thought of freedom, and may have gone too far when I embraced little Mrs Hurd, much to her bewilderment, and asked her whether she did the Hokey Cokey. In any event it's been the gamma rays and bread and water ever since.

The real fairy on the Christmas tree as far as M. was concerned was Basil Bush, our American ally, whose courage in invading the equivalent of Brixton has earned him her undying love. When Mr Pockface Noriega finally strolled in and handed himself over to the Pope, M. was fit to be tied. Even from my den I could hear her dialling the fifteen digits necessary for the White House, and her roar of passionate condemnation. 'How dare he interfere in your internal affairs? The one I have here is enough trouble. You wouldn't know him, he's called Runcie.' (Even in his Christmas sermon, Boris tells me, old Snaggleteeth had tried to nip a bit out of her ankle, moaning on about riff-raff living in cardboard boxes, as if the Boss was in some way responsible if people can't pay their wine merchant.) In the end the Boss volunteered to lend Basil the SAS to flush out the Papal Nuncio and his acne-victim friend.

You probably noticed that thanks to M. and little Major the sales started long before Christmas. Maurice's friend Mr Rothschild who runs the bespoke tailoring business in Regent Street says the arse is falling out of his trousers, business is terrible, so we might pick up a few bargains in the off-the-peg department. I had a dekko in their window last night on my way back from the Club, and they have waterproof tartan trousers knocked down to £399.99, which seems a snip in anybody's language.

Thank you very much for my gloves. Very thoughtful of you. They are an almost perfect fit.

See you at Maurice's farewell Rotary on the 5th.

The Old Decayed,

DENIS

Dear Bill,

Did you see the Boss on the box with that smarmy Leprechaun Wogan? It all came about because last time the Commies at the BBC sent round Dimbleby to do the interview and he was so bloody rude and wouldn't allow her to finish her speeches that they lodged a formal complaint with Pegleg Hussey the Chairman threatening him with privatisation unless he made amends. The result was a special 40-minute prime-time love-in with Wogan, questions submitted in advance, all the top brass in the hospitality room rubbing their hands and grovelling.

I thought it was fairly nauseating myself especially when he asked her (to cue) what her most worrying moment had been and she launched into the old Falkands routine for the 497th time. You may have noticed too how yours truly's name was taken in vain purely for the sake of comic relief. Apparently whenever DT was mentioned some little monkey held up a board in front of the audience with LAUGH on it, the Boss joining in the fun and making out that I was some kind of lovable old relic like the Elephant Man whose antics over the years had endeared him to the entire nation.

We had hardly unpacked our overnight bags following the New Year Winter-Break at Chequers when little Fowler rang saying he had something very urgent to confide. To be frank I'd never really taken him on board as a bona fide human being. He reminded me of that accountant friend of Maurice's in the velvet-collared overcoat who was always in attendance when we tried to wind up the double-glazing factory. Perfectly inoffensive but no one ever knew what his name was.

Anyway, Fowler came in looking very tense saying he would rather speak to Margaret alone if that was all right. 'Don't be silly, Norman!' the Boss rapped, plainly sensing that something ominous was in the offing. 'Denis is one of us.' At this, tears came into Fowler's eyes and he began to pour out a flood of guff about how he had served the Boss faithfully ever since he could remember and he never had any thanks though he did not expect it, it was enough for him to serve. 'Come to the point, Fowler,' the Boss interpolated, drumming her

'. . . Apparently whenever DT was mentioned some little monkey held up a board in front of the audience with LAUGH on it . . .'

fingers impatiently on the scrambler telephone, 'there is work to be done.'

This seemed only to intensify poor Fowler's emotions and mopping his eyes with a blue silk handkerchief he extracted a rather tattered photograph from his wallet. 'Look, Prime Minister,' he sobbed. 'These are my two little girls, Sabena and Ramona. Do you know when I last had time to take them on my knee and read them a bedtime story from Old Mother Goose?'

The Boss seemed to think that some reference to herself was being made, for her eyes glinted with resentment. 'I have never listened to such sentimental nonsense. Ever!' she snapped. 'You have been given plenty of time to devote to your family. We all of us have. Look at me, I work much, much harder than all of you men put together, but you do not hear Denis complaining that he is neglected. Do you, Denis? Denis! I am asking you a question.'

'No, no, of course not, dear,' I replied, passing poor Fowler a shot of the electric soup which he gratefully gulped back.

'Denis and I see a great deal of each other,' she persevered, 'and always, regularly at 12.30 every night, we compare notes on what has transpired during the day. I commend this practice to you and your wife.' But poor Fowler had had enough. 'I resign, I resign!' he cried. 'I am at breaking point. Cynthia is threatening a divorce. You can stuff your red boxes!' With this he stormed out, knocking over my glass and splashing its priceless contents all over the wall to wall.

'Some of them cannot stand the pace,' said the Boss firmly, after the dust had settled. 'It is better for them to go before they finally crack. Luckily that will not happen in my case. I have been given extra strength for the task ahead.'

Munster's coup meanwhile gains momentum. He never forgave Margaret for passing him over in favour of Young during the big election shindig when there was all that trouble about which ad agency to use. His ploy is to come on strong as Son of Enoch, uttering dire warnings about the Yellow Peril from Hong Kong swamping our green and pleasant land. A whole lot of the less civilised backbenchers have now rallied to his banner, so they've sent out greaser Hurd to reassure the Chinks and make sure that not too many of them apply for visas. (Though as a matter of fact a lot of these Chinese chaps have settled in very well over here, witness our good caretaker at Chequers, Mr Wu.)

I'm sorry you weren't able to join us for Maurice's New Year celebrations at the Ramada Dirty Duck. Quite a lot of people cried off at the last moment, leaving me, Maurice, Maurice's new dry cleaning lady and Tubby Hotchkiss to spread ourselves in the Mountbatten Ballroom, which Maurice had optimistically reserved for the occasion. Tubby, as you probably know, is confined to a wheelchair nowadays and makes if anything less sense than he did when he was still walking about. Maurice's lady complained of swollen ankles that she thinks are brought on by the greenhouse effect, and Maurice was affected by a rare twinge of conscience about having booked the ballroom on the Major's American Express card the week before while he was in the Gents.

Yours apoplectically,

DENIS

51

Dear Bill,
I have been trying to keep out of range of the Gamma Rays
since the ID cards issue blew up again. You recall the trouble
we were in before, after she sent Hurd out on to the doorstep
to announce that strong measures would be taken to stem the
tide of hooliganism? The result was her crazy ID card scheme.
I told her, as I may say did several million other people, that
it was totally pointless to expect those yobbos and skinheads
to queue up outside the ground with little bits of plastic, but
she wouldn't hear a word against the idea. Anyway, finally
this striped-trousered judge, who has been looking into the
shambles that is soccer, has come out very firmly against it.
Cue for the Smellysocks to rise as a man and scream for her
to start eating her words, which needless to say she refused to
do.

In the circs, I deemed it only prudent to refrain from any
hint of 'I told you so'. (Incidentally, you may have seen in the
small print that that bearded prat Branson, out of whose rear
quarters at one time the sun was thought to shine, has folded
up his Anti-Litter League which the Boss had entrusted with
the job of cleaning up Britain. So another scrawny old chicken
has come home to roost.)

Poor Mrs Van der Kaffirbasher has sent a somewhat
desperate SOS asking me to look out for 'a nice bungalow-style
property in downtown Dulwich, ideally with separate maid
quarters and kennel facilities for my darling Rotties'. She
blames the Boss for her failure to stand up to these 'Coons and
Commies in the Commonwealth' who have brought about the
downfall of her homeland.

'The last straw, dear Denis, is the way the traitor de Klerk
has failed completely to supervise your cricket tour. It grieves
my heart, Denis, to see brave Mike Gatting and his men being
harassed wherever they go by crowds of chattering monkeys
dancing up and down with their placards. I tell you in the days
of Dr Verwoerd (God rest his noble soul) it would never have
been allowed to happen. And now they are going to allow the

'. . . *that bearded prat Branson, out of whose rear quarters at one time the sun was thought to shine, has folded up his Anti-Litter League . . .*'

kaffirs to buy land in our special white areas: that is why, Denis, Horst and I have decided to spend our twilight years in Great Britain as your neighbours, for it truly breaks our heart to see what is being done to this beautiful country in the name of progress.'

Talking of Dulwich I have been forced to put my foot down after Furniss pointed out that thanks to Major's incompetence and total failure to bring down interest rates the value of the property had fallen by at least 20% – Furniss said it made no sense at all to have a lot of money tied up in a diminishing asset and that after seeing the Boss on Wogan it was quite obvious that she was going to carry on until she dropped and that I should put Dulwich up for sale and put our names down for a service flat complete with special facilities for the senile and incontinent. I said I would be prepared to consider such a contingency if somewhere could be found within staggering distance of the RAC. Anyway, I am going to have a drink with Maurice's estate agent friend Mr Goldsack on Tuesday to talk it over.

Talking of Maurice, I had a call from that nursing home near Tonbridge to say that he had been re-admitted suffering from head wounds. Apparently when the Great Gale struck he was in his cellar trying to find my Christmas present. All the lights went out leaving him to grope about in the pitch dark. Eventually he found a bottle, but when he took a swig, it turned out to be paraffin. Choking and spluttering with nausea and fury combined, he shot out of the house only to be struck on the head by his satellite dish which had been blown loose by the hurricane force winds.

Yours aye,

DENIS

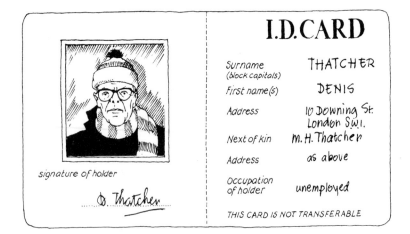

I.D.CARD

Surname (block capitals)	THATCHER
First name(s)	DENIS
Address	10 Downing St. London S.W.1.
Next of kin	M.H. Thatcher
Address	as above
Occupation of holder	unemployed

signature of holder

D. Thatcher

THIS CARD IS NOT TRANSFERABLE

16 FEBRUARY 1990

Dear Bill,

I'm sorry I had to leave the table at the RAC the other night. I intended to return, but Mrs Van der K. turned out to have arrived at Heathrow, accompanied by her two Rotties, Kruger and Smuts, en route for Crufts, and had run into a bit of strife with Immigration. Both dogs were in quarantine and Mrs Van der K. herself had been strip-searched by an Indian security lady for whom she had conceived a very violent dislike. I was the knight in shining armour who was expected to drive out to Heathrow with a warrant from the Boss ordering the security lady to be summarily executed and Mrs Van der K. and the dogs driven into central London in an armed motorcade. I fear it may be the end of a long and beautiful friendship.

When I tried to explain that it was not as easy as she seemed to think, the good lady exploded with rage. 'Denis! You and your wife, I suspected all along, are dangerous Communists. I have watched with alarm her squalid romance with that awful Russian man with the disfiguring birthmark. How you could stand idly by I have often wondered, but I expect at your advanced age you are too decrepit to fulfil your marital duties or to feel any resentment if others fulfil them for you. Now this woman your wife cannot wait to come to South Africa to shake the bloodstained hand of the Great Judas himself, F.W. de Klerk. You could not bear our beloved homeland to be such a paradise, you had to drag it down to the same sink of anarchy and filth as I find exists here. Well, a few of us intend to establish our own Fortress Fatherland with our Fuhrer Eugene de Terreblanche. No Communists admitted, so you and your wife need not apply for a visa when the taps of the bloodbath are turned on. The golf clubs you left behind after your last visit will be ceremonially burnt by our loyal houseboys. Dorcas was horrified to find an empty bottle under your bed. How repulsive! Horst and I always suspected that while masquerading as a decent supporter of South Africa you were in fact a secret drunkard.'

'. . . Mrs Van der K. turned out to have arrived at Heathrow,
accompanied by her two Rotties, Kruger and Smuts . . .'

At this point there was the sound of a scuffle and the poor woman was dragged screaming from the telephone, much to my relief as it was by this time gone two and they were closing the Club. When I eventually found my way home I did my best to raise the matter with the Mem, but got my ear pretty severely bitten off for my pains.

I ran into Gascoigne-Pees at Huntercombe. You remember, I am sure, that he is quite a big noise in the Hush-hush Department, i.e. MI5. We had a few drinks, and he got very hot under the collar about this Colin Wallace chap trying to stir the shit over the so-called Dirty Tricks. The Ministry chaps, he argued, were only doing their duty, drawing the public's attention to the fact that the Labour Party were all hand in glove with the IRA, that Wilson was a Russian spy and up to no good with that secretary woman of his, and that Heath was a poof. Later on he became less reasonable, downing trebles at a gulp. A nasty glint came into his eye, he gripped me by the lapel and said: 'It's like this, Thatcher. You tell your little lady we don't want any busybodies digging through the files, okay? Otherwise it might come to light just who benefited from all this, if you take my meaning. Wilson kaput, Heath kaput, who comes strolling on to the field to the cheers of the great unwashed? You tell her Mum's the word, all right old boy?' His grip on my throat was by this time quite painful, making it difficult to breathe, but I said I would pass on his views to the appropriate quarter, whereupon he let go and lurched from the room, snatching his crutch from the hatstand.

Tempers have been getting a bit frayed at this end over the big Kremlin AGM. Ingham, M's propaganda chief, ran amok at a press lunch, and basted the reptiles in emotional mood, telling them they were all liars and yobs, and bursting into tears when he recalled the good old days of British journalism when he himself wore the green eyeshade. The real reason for this was that despite having been issued with a full-colour press pack in words of one syllable explaining how the Boss had single-handedly rid the earth of the scourge of Communism, not one of them had given an inch to the story, pretending instead that Gorbo had done it all off his own bat. To cap it all, Ingham had to call off the Boss's Mandela press conference on Sunday because she was literally speechless with rage because the Great Redeemer had called for the Armed Struggle to continue.

The latest in the Maurice saga is that he was in the throes of a reconciliation with Miss Mifsud, the Air Malta lady, which had reached a delicate point, requiring Maurice for some reason to sleep in the greenhouse. During the full and frank exchanges that led up to this, Maurice had omitted to listen to the weather forecast and in the second hurricane the entire structure became airborne, landing untouched in a swimming pool next door much to Maurice's bewilderment.

Any chance of your joining me on a day's hover to Dieppe to taste the Pernod Nouveau?

Yrs a la carte,

DENIS

10 Downing Street
Whitehall

2 MARCH 1990

Dear Bill,

Fancy bumping into you at the Savoy! I'd no idea you were a member of that particular Order. A very handsome apron, and from the noise emanating from the Iolanthe Suite it sounded to be a pretty good binge. As you may have gathered from the blatts, the Mem and I were guests at a little celebration of Sailor Ted's Forty Years Up the Mast. When the stiffy came in a month or so back, my inclination was to tell the fellow where he could put it. I mean, after the things he's said about the Boss, how he could have the nerve to invite us seemed to me v. rich. M. was of a like mind and was in the middle of doodling on it with her Highliter when little Tinker Bell, our media adviser, minced in with the clippings. They were, he said, not of the brightest. Poll Tax was proving a pretty good turkey, there was some reluctance among the unwashed to see M. as the Champion of Mandela and Saviour of Eastern Europe, surely E. Heath's Bunfeast a golden opportunity to take the front pages and establish her as a woman of magnanimity and statesmanship who did not bear a grudge.

So it was that we found ourselves queuing up on the stairs of the River Room together with old skullface Home, Fatty Prior and various of M's other liquidees, waiting to shake the powdered hand of the Old Man of the Sea. Sweetness and light had been pretty firmly hammered into us by Bell, and Margaret was wearing the fixed grin she normally keeps for pressing flesh at the Commonwealth Conference. 'Ted!' she soothed, 'many, many congratulations. So many years of loyal service to our party!' 'Thank you very much,' came the abrupt reply. 'Extremely good of you to come. And this must be your husband. How do you do? You'll find the drinks straight ahead. There's fruit cup, and spirits have to be paid for. Ha ha.' At this he revealed all his yellow teeth, his shoulders began to heave, and I propelled Margaret forward into the reception before there was any unpleasantness.

It was not unlike going to hell. All sorts of people one imagined to be dead, in most cases by Margaret's hand, standing there and leering. Old Carrington, for one, bowled up and slapped me on the back, spectacles agleam, and congratulated me on my stamina. Did I remember the time he shouted at the Boss over Rhodesia so loudly that the policeman came in and fingered his lapel? Could I imagine Hurd doing that kind of thing? He laughed a lot, said how glad he was to be out of it, and that it didn't look as if I'd have to suffer for very much longer the way things were going. Then one I couldn't remember at all, but I think may have been Pym, came up and said the day he'd been sacked had been the happiest day of his life. He and his wife had gone out to a restaurant in Abingdon and got completely sloshed, then came home and set fire to a big picture of the Boss they had cut out of the *Illustrated London News*.

Just my luck when we sat down therefore to find myself next to the blue-jowled Munster, sniggering a good deal at M's discomfiture as she forked in the smoked meats and listened abstractly to the skeletal chatter of her predecessor of the Hirsel, recounting from what I could catch, how he'd bagged two seagulls and a shrike, whatever that is, and his wife had cooked them for supper and found them rather bony.

Whatever you say about Munster, he is very sound on the BBC, especially that chap with the beard and the funny accent they have on in the mornings. He told me, which I didn't know, that Redbeard, or whatever his name is, is a member of the Communist Party and writes for the *Daily Worker* under the name of Moscow Mike, and that the Scots woman he is on with was Life President of the Lesbian Anarchist League until it was closed down by the police. He had all this from M's friend Woodrow Wyatt, that fat man with the wet cigar and the double-breasted pinstripe who runs a lot of betting shops. I wrote it all down on the back of my menu to show to the Boss afterwards, but by that time Ted was on his feet with the reptiles flashing away all round him, hoping for what is called a good photo opportunity of the Boss doing the Gamma Rays.

However, all that passed off without further trouble, and Margaret went home convinced that the hatchet was buried, at least as far as the public was concerned, and that E. Heath had been melted by her gracious presence. Picture her distress, then, when we turned on Sir Alastair Burnet's Newsround, to see a post-prandial interview filmed after our departure with our wobbly-jowled friend now flushed with fine wines, putting the boot in as before on a variety of pretexts. 'Isolated from Europe, isolated from America, what's she going to do?' What she did immediately was to snap off the remote control and give Bell the most terrible bollocking down the blower.

A propos the Hun, the Nation has me to thank for putting a bit of spine into poor Hurd. Despite his white hair and stooping demeanour, he is not old enough to remember as we do two world wars brought about directly by the Boche. No wonder that as soon as the Russkies relax their grip, up pops Fatty Kohl calling for Lebensraum and a United Fatherland. As I explained to Hurd, the only language they understand is armed intervention, or failing that the medicine old Bomber Harris used to spoon out day after day and night after night until they began to see sense.

Have you had your Poll Tax form? I can't see what all the fuss is about. Do you remember Simonds-Gooding from Burmah days? He inherited quite a large place near Crowhurst as well as a comfortable house in Belgrave Square. I saw him at Trumper's the other day, and he was absolutely cock-a-hoop. He said he was looking at something like two grand a year less than he was paying on rates and gave me a cigar.

So why all the palaver? Furniss suggests I call Dulwich mine for the purposes of the form, with myself as sole occupant. Alas, would that it were so!

Yours on a tight leash,

DENIS

'. . . He said he was looking at something like two grand a year less than he was paying on rates and gave me a cigar . . .'

Dear Bill,

Your petition, you will be glad to know, was finally delivered to Number Ten by your friend Mrs Rattner-Leng, who was let in through the gates while her fellow-protesters were made to wait at the railings. Five thousand signatures, smudged as they may have been in some cases with drink, certainly bore evidence to the strength of feeling about Margaret's Poll Tax in your neck of the woods.

Giglamps Baker, who played a big part in dreaming it all up, continues to push the line that all the opposition is coming from the Red Rentamob. I tried to get across to him that quite a lot of our sort of people were up in arms at having to pay more when the whole idea was that the scroungers were the ones who would be squealing. The Boss, who was by this stage in Bunker mode, repeated: 'It is all the fault of the profligate Labour Councils, they must be held to account and seen for the extravagant managers they are.'

I pointed out that Royal Tunbridge Wells was not best known as a hotbed of Revolutionary Socialism, and that Mrs Posner, the woman we met with your accountant friend Pringle when we were washed out at Sandwich, and who lives in a largish property on Mount Ephraim with her batty step-daughter and her live-in nurse Mrs Cobb, is going to have to fork out almost as much as she did when she was paying the rates.

At this Margaret hit the roof, fair screaming at me that she'd never realised she was married for all these years to a paid-up member of the Marxist-Leninist League, no wonder I had refused to be positively vetted and it was a well-known fact that people of my kind took to drink because of a personality defect.

You will gather from this that shot and shell are rather whistling through the rigging just at present, and things were not improved when that smooth-talking city man Slater Walker handed in his cards at the weekend saying he wanted to spend more time with his family. Having witnessed the final

'. . . I had a very angry call late on Friday from that Gippo at Harrods who's always giving us crocodile-skin wallets . . .'

parting of the ways, Walker's statement to the press that it had all been very amicable brought a wryish smile to my lips. M. was in fighting mood, quoting extensively from the Bard to the effect that those who had no stomach for the fight should get out of the kitchen before the ship went down. Heath was behind this, Walker had never been one of us, she had sent him off to Wales where he had done nothing but harm, look at the floods there had been etc, etc.

To put the tin hat on it, Heseltine got up at Halitosis Hall, bold as brass, and spoke in Margaret's defence to tumultuous applause, a sure sign in M's view that the knife will be between her shoulder blades before the leaves are on the trees.

I had a very angry call late on Friday from that little Gippo at Harrods who's always giving us crocodile-skin wallets. Ridley had done everything he could to silence the tall German who owns the *Observer*, but the day came when he had to do a deal with the Gippo Twins that if Old Bill didn't feel their collars he could let out a somewhat unflattering report on their business methods. Little Muhammed, always an excitable fellow, was near to hysteria on the blower: 'What you people are doing, I bloody well want to know' – I omit the obscenities – 'My brother and I bring plenty business to this expletive deleted country, lots of expletive deleted money, and what you expletive deleteds do to us?'

I pointed out that there was no question of proceedings against them 'due to lack of evidence', that being called a crook in the House of Commons was something we all had to put up with nowadays, and they still had Harrods. Our dusky friend then began to speak very incoherently to the accompaniment of breaking furniture in the background and would-be restraining cries from his brother Sali, mentioning the boy Mark, the Sultan of Brunei, the Boss and how this could all blow up in our expletive deleted faces if we didn't make a public apology in the High Court and have the tall German assassinated. Munster came into it too somewhere but I can't quite recall how.

The only good news was about Brer Scargill and the tainted Libyan money. My MI5 friend Gascoigne-Pees tells me they paid the one with the beard to blow the whistle on him to distract attention from the Poll Tax. I'm sorry to see Greville Wynne turned his toes up. I always liked him.

I'm putting together a few days' golf in Northern Ireland to coincide with Comrade Mandela's State Visit. Any chance of your being let off the leash?

Yours as the water rises,

DENIS

30 MARCH 1990

Dear Bill,

I tried to ring on Budget Eve to warn you about the hike on Electric Soup, but only got your answering machine with the artificial rotty bark. Personally I managed to ferry a low-loader full of crates into the Store at Dulwich, and being a fair man I might be prepared to let you have a doz at half the official increase. Major's behaviour on cigarettes was quite unspeakable. I saw him as he scurried out of the Sanctum after giving the Boss her exclusive preview, tapped the fag I was smoking and raised my eyebrows. Little bugger blew out his cheeks and shook his head. So much for trust between next door neighbours.

There was universal gloom at the Club when I called in with my empties. That stockjobber friend of yours – Millington Drake? Rubinstein? No matter – was looking absolutely ashen, on his second bottle of Pernod and saying Major had funked the jump and that what was needed was a shilling on the Income Tax to show that we meant business. I couldn't understand this, economics with me always tending to go in one ear and out the other, but when I called in on Furniss the next day to have a look at my Deposit Account he poohpoohed Major too, and said all this Tessa business was pissing in the wind and I'd be well advised to keep all my various nesteggs in their Golden Calf Extra Money Cheque Book Account at 15¾% net.

Most of Margaret's energies, I am glad to say, have been devoted to digging up some filth on Heseltine. Tarzan is playing it very cleverly, according to Bell, pledging his undying devotion to the Boss at every juncture, and when asked whether he wants the job saying that he 'cannot forsee the circumstances when he would challenge her'. You probably remember that slippery little fellow Oddling-Smee who was after Wino Henderson's job as Treasurer of the Sports Committee at Burmah. He always made a point of prefacing his reading of the Minutes with elaborate compliments about how much we all appreciated his efforts; at the same time he was

'. . . said . . . I'd be well advised to keep all my various nest-eggs in their *Golden Calf Extra Money Cheque Book Account* at 15¾% net. . . .'

tipping off the *Rangoon Herald* about the poor state of the pavilion and how the billiard table was rotted with brandy.

All MI5 have picked up so far is a shady relationship at the University with a dubious German called Labovich who published Blue magazines, but if you ask me the Dirty Tricks Mob who are notoriously fickle in their loyalties may well be going over to Tarzan. When I got back to the Den the other night the Harrods File had definitely been interfered with and felt to me to be still warm from the photocopier. The golden golf club that little Mumu Fayed gave me when we went to America had also been taken out of its case and stood against the wall under a light.

Right now they're having a big post-mortem on Mid-Staffs. Baker, Clarke, and Smarmy C. all insisted that the Poll Tax would have to be changed and that the only possibility was to go behind Major's back and plug Education into the National Debt so that Local Authorities would only have to pay for the dustbin men. The Boss would hear none of it, repeating over and over again that the Community Charge was perfectly fair and would only serve to highlight the profligacy of Labour Councils who squandered money on gay bus-shelters. I then heard her quite clearly through two doors laying into Baker for personally losing the by-election. 'Over-confidence, I've said it again and again, Mr Baker! How could you lose one of the jewels in our crown? If only I had gone, but you advised me not to!'

This was not strictly accurate, as I knew from having listened on the kitchen extension to Bell on Disasters. Market research had shown that there was consumer resistance to M's Angel of Mercy campaign, whereby the Product had been shown arriving at air-crashes, fires and football stadia etc, and that this was measurably curtailing her shelf-life. The long and the short of it was she should stay away from any disaster, particularly electoral, and leave Floods in Wales and Chernobyl-style scenarios to the Royals.

I got a very curious letter from Maurice, typed by his Air Malta lady, asking me whether I could find out from Waddington, the bald one who took over from Hurd, about who exactly was on the black list for this new War Crimes Retrospective at the Old Bailey. Apparently an uncle of his in Rotherham has got his knickers in a knot about a part-time job he took in Poland in the forties. As he is Chief Water Rat in the local Worshipful Order of Buffaloes and a pillar of the Town Council, I could appreciate Maurice's concern for his elderly relative should, in Hailsham's rather unhappy phrase, 'they be looking for someone to crucify'.

A propos don't the East German Tories look to you a very rum bunch?

Yours on the departure platform,

DENIS

Dear Bill,

I had a mysterious call some time back from Old Oyster-Eyes who I hadn't seen since the time he was shifted out of the bed next to the door in the Cabinet, and we went out and got hogwhimpering drunk at the East India and Sports. Would I care to join him and a few friends at the Carlton Club for a spot of lunch – 'to chat about the old days'? Boris immediately smelt a rat, but you know I'll do anything for a few free ones. So yesterday found me spruce and thirsty on the steps of the Carlton on the stroke of half past eleven.

Oyster-Eyes was already ensconced in a little private bar just off the main concourse and out of sight of the three times lifesize portrait of Margaret that hangs over the stairs. 'Ah, Thatcher!' he cried, leaping to his feet and spreading his arms wide in welcome. 'These are stirring times, what?' I was hoping he would offer me a drink, but instead he pointed to a brick on a silver tray on the table beside him. 'Chucked in by the mob through the door of the downstairs Gents on Saturday afternoon. Old Rusbridger who cleans the silver had the fright of his life. Caught him smack on the back of the neck just as he was doing his flies up.'

It transpired that while you and I were pottering about at Huntercombe last weekend the capital erupted in flames. Very much what you and I used to get up to on Boat Race Night, but ugly in the hands of the wrong people, i.e. every Trot and Bolshie not in Broadcasting House with nothing to do that afternoon.

A dry smacking of my lips brought Whitelaw back to his senses, and I was soon plugged into the Electric Soup, the world looking a good deal rosier. 'This Waddington chap they've got now,' I opined when the dust had settled. 'He doesn't seem to me to be up to much. In the old days we would have rounded up all those Reds and given them what you used to call a Short Sharp Shock.' 'Thing is, Thatcher,' the old boy ruminated rumpling his chins. 'It's not quite as simple as that. Chaps overseas with money in the City take a rather dim view

'. . . "Ah, Thatcher!" he cried, leaping to his feet and spreading
his arms wide in welcome . . .'

of burning motor cars. Don't ask me why, I've never
understood the Stock Market, but there is something called
Confidence, a fragile bloom at the best of times, and for many
years of course Margaret has been superb, quite superb in,
ahem, tending that bloom. Don't think for one moment we
don't all appreciate what she did. Another drink?'

As Old Silvester tottered over with a second jug of the Club Soup, it struck me that there was something a little eerie in the use of the past tense by our fishy-faced friend. ' "Did"? ' I asked.

'We must look ahead to ninety-two, Thatcher. You will be a very old man, drink probably getting on top of you, memory going, an embarrassment to your family and friends, in no state to be capering about for the press monkeys with all their clever-dick questions.'

At this point the door of our little sanctum opened, and Mogadon stuck his head round. 'How's it going?' he said to my surprise. 'Come along in, Geoffrey. We were just talking about the old days. Drink?' Mogadon accepted a bottle of Auld Jimmy Carter's Kentucky Rye, and we were joined by the Senior Back Bencher, someone called, I think, Onsleigh-Bagshott, a pretty depressing cove and clearly in the grip of a fierce hangover. Conversation was then fairly torpid till about half past two when we went in to lunch, Howe having tried something about some new curtains his wife had just had made, and Bagshott telling us how he'd lost four hooks fishing in the Doon, wherever that is.

Usual disgusting potted shrimps covered with half an inch of rancid butter, followed by Graveyard Stew served by some old boy who had clearly only recently been released into the community from one of our geriatric institutions. Whitelaw chomped away for a bit, Bagshott's hangover clearly getting worse and worse as he tried the Hair of the Dog in vain in the form of silver beaker after silver beaker of the Club's Spanish Infuriator.

Finally Whitelaw came to the point. 'Reason we asked you here, Thatcher, is that it is plain to all of us that Margaret has been, ahem, rowing the boat, pedalling away, well beyond the allotted half hour: superb contribution, let no one underestimate, etc.' At this Howe and Bagshott mumbled agreement through their mouthfuls of stew. 'But now the Boating Pond Superintendent is calling "Come in, Margaret, your time is up"! You, Thatcher, know your wife better than any of us' (I thought at this point I heard Mogadon say 'Thank God' into his bread roll but decided to ignore it, the poor sod having quite enough to put up with in that department himself, and the Elder Statesman continued on his Olympian way).

'We feel that she is the last person however to lay down her oars on hearing the call "Come in, your time is up", however peremptory the tone. But Margaret is a compassionate woman, a woman capable of very deep feeling where personal matters are concerned, witness her tears when your beloved son was lost in the desert.' I refrained from giving any view on the Boy Mark and waved for another jug from the walking mummy. 'This is where you come in, Thatcher. Geoffrey here has roughed something out for you to say, I'm sure Bell and Co will polish it up and put in a few jokes. That man in the dressing gown can help if you like. Geoffrey?'

Poor Mogadon was then obliged to pull a tattered envelope out of his pocket, and to intone as follows: 'I am an old man. I am sick. I am tired. I implore you, Margaret, to have pity on a faithful spouse who accompanied you along life's nature trail at considerable expense to his wallet and personal dignity. You are at your prime, with many years . . .' At this Onsleigh-Bagshott gave a grim laugh before clutching his forehead in pain, 'still to enjoy at the top. But I plead with you to make this great sacrifice for the sake of our marriage.'

All was silent apart from Whitelaw munching on the stew and the slow returning tread of our ancient waiter. Howe kept the envelope in his hand, blinking at me to see how it had gone down. 'Surely something along those lines will strike a chord?' 'It certainly would. A chord of B bloody sharp major and jolly loud. "You, Denis, have let yourself go. You are a pathetic wreck. You have brought this on yourself by your excessive self-indulgence. Pull yourself together. I have no sympathy with whingers, whiners or defeatists." Read it to her yourself.'

Faces fell at this, and the Club Cherry Crumble failed to do anything to dispel the mood of gloom that ensued. As we dispersed I distinctly heard Onsleigh-Bagshott, who was peeing in the next stall to Whitelaw, saying it looked as though it was going to have to be the Ceausescu Treatment after all.

Have you got the tickets for Portugal? Your man de Freitas at Student Travel International said we would qualify as minors if we showed a local library ticket. Could you get a couple from your friend Commander Waddilove?

Yours enjoying a last cigarette,

DENIS

Dear Bill,

Given the propensity of the drowning to clutch at straws or so we are told, it is not to be wondered at that the champagne corks were cracking in little Renton's office after the Honkers Debate. Poor Munster, having led a gallant attack on the side of sanity in order to hold back the Yellow Peril, had only managed to muster fifty or so brave and true Englishmen to stand behind him on the bridge, and like the Roman chappie of yore, raise two fingers to the invading barbarians. Alas, on this occasion the bridge collapsed, and the Chinese are to flood in unimpeded.

For a former airline pilot with so little savoir-faire in the Saloon Bar, Munster has a vein of decency which you don't often find among the lower orders. He pointed out, as far as I could determine from the report in the *Daily Telegraph*, that you can't have a lot of so-called British Citizens cheering for Hong Kong in the Test Match. (This obviously applied to the mad Mullahs of Bradford, crying for the blood of that awful paperback writer Solomon Rushton, though after the things he's said about Margaret I must confess I'd be right behind them.) If you travel in the Supporters' Charabanc, Munster meant, it's damn bad form to have an alien flag smuggled up your jumper and brandish it about when the other fellows walk out to the crease. What it put me in mind of was that fellow from Marketing Research at Burmah – Havergal? Sherrin? Some name like that – who had a French wife who used to run amok in the Rothman's Superthin Box at Twickers whenever the Frogs scrambled through for a try. I seem to recall Prosser-Cluff taking him for a walk along the touchline during half-time and telling him he'd be wise to leave Madame at home the following year.

Talking of that sort of thing, did you see Pillock giving his clenched fist to Mundella at the Nuremberg Rally out at Wembley? M., as you may well imagine, was fit to be tied when the BBC decided to show all four hours of it, claiming it was entirely non-political, and poor peg-leg Hussey had his Sunday lunch pretty satisfactorily ruined by a personal call

*'. . . I seem to recall Prosser-Cluff taking him for a walk along
the touchline during half-time and telling him he'd be wise to
leave Madame at home the following year . . .'*

from the Boss saying that he must call it off or face the consequences. Given Margaret's lack of divisions on the ground just
at present, these consequences amounted to a public bollocking about Reds in the Godslot, after which the morning radio
show with Brian Redbeard, which sets the Boss up in a good
fiery rage for the rest of the day, will in future only have Tory
Thoughts and that sweet old Rabbi who does the jokes.

What really got M's goat during the Mundella Show was
when the old boy, who, as M. points out, owes his freedom
entirely to her, had the brazen neck to tell her that she
wouldn't be welcome in the Land of the Free. 'How dare he?'
she fumed, turning down the sound on her remote control
device in a vicious way. 'The sooner he gets back to South

Africa and stops the awful bloodshed between black and black, instead of lecturing others about their moral duties, Denis, the better. I have a letter from my old friend Sir Laurence van der Pump telling me all about it. Mundella is a Communist, no better than the IRA; the one we should be supporting is Mr Bloodylazy, King of the Zulus. He has never condoned violence, except against Mundella. I am sure he is our man.'

As if to confirm this view, the telephone beside my bed jangled at four a.m. with a call from Mrs Van der K., now all packed up and ready to move to Hong Kong. 'We have not been able to sleep all night, Denis. When we saw your Mr Kinnock on the TV holding up his fist in the Communist salute we knew the writing was on the wall. Your Margaret is a very irresponsible woman. It is all very well for her, she can sling her handbag over her arm and retire. Britain will have a Communist Government, with Winnie and Glenys hanging out their washing on the balcony at Buckingham Palace.' At that moment there was barking from the Rotties as they seemed to have caught another intruder, causing Mrs Van der K. to abandon the call to go and see what she'd got in the mantrap.

I'm glad you got my card from Bermuda. Mother Bush was very good company, knocking back the snorts like a trooper while Basil went off on his morning job with eighteen security men. He graciously agreed to a photo opportunity of him and me holding each other up on the Royal Bermuda and Ancient but M's continual whingeing on about the Grand Old Days with Hopalong seemed to grate on poor Basil, and very understandably in my view. Imagine her displeasure if some foreign Johnny turned up to have his picture taken at Number Ten and kept on saying what a wonderful man Sailor Ted was.

I think autumn in Dulwich is pretty firmly on the cards now, though that fool Bell is still toying with an Assassination Attempt scenario to be handled by the SAS, who may, I think, have lost faith in the Boss after she failed to bring them in to zap the rooftop hooligans at Strangeways. Waddington entre nous is so wet you could use him to wipe the bar down.

Talking of which what are your Bank Holiday plans? Would it amuse you to get pissed with Whitelaw at a Health Farm in Buckinghamshire?

Yours aromatherapeutically,

DENIS

74

Dear Bill,

Thank you for your commiserations. I had pinned a great deal on the Poll Tax Catastrophe That Never Was and I have only just returned to my senses following the Wake at the RAC where I was joined by Whitelaw and Onslow-Bagshott and we polished off everything the club possessed in the way of pre-phylloxera Embalming Fluid.

As you know the hope had been for an out and out disaster at the Local Elections, leading to a dignified resignation on the part of my better half. However thanks to that freckled knob-head Kinnock we are now practically back to square one, with little Bell full of good cheer and talking about a Perrier-style relaunch of the product, a full-scale zapping operation on poor Tarzan, in other words back in the slammer for the duration.

Baker came round,

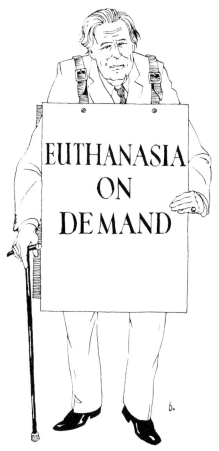

'. . . an article by that TV Johnny with the ballerina wife about how one ought to be able to bump off a loved one with a packet of sleepers . . .'

smarmy as ever, with the results, showing that apart from three London boroughs where palms had been pretty liberally greased, our side had lost hands down. 'A triumph indeed, Prime Minister!' he beamed, running his fingers over his self-basting hair. 'The pollsters have been confounded. They predicted a fifty-six per cent swing to the enemy; it is merely fifty-three per cent! I congratulate you, Leader, and more so because this will finally put an end to the hysteria among our rank and file calling for a new broom.' 'What do you mean, a new broom?' 'Well, there has been a great deal of damaging talk about the Leadership Issue, which will now, I am sure, be silenced. Talk, Prime Minister, about your unsuitability to lead us into the next election. Many people, some of them quite senior people, have been saying that you are a spent force, a liability to the party and so forth. All this will now be revealed in the light of this victory, to have been hysterical and misguided. I refer, of course, to disloyal speculation that it might be time for you to step down and give way to someone less tarnished by recent events and better qualified to mobilise Tory support . . .'

'The Community Charge is here to stay, if that is what you mean,' Margaret intervened, looking up from her Red Box. 'The results in Ealing, Westminster and Wandsworth show that people have got the message: high-spending Labour Councils will be punished for their profligacy.' 'Quite so, quite so, Prime Minister, though naturally there have been disappointments, as at Bradford. But these ought not to revive wild surmise throughout the length and breadth of the country as to the possibility of your leaving us in July to devote yourself to your husband in his declining years . . .' As I myself was perusing with great interest an article in the *Sunday Telegraph* by that TV Johnny with the ballerina wife about how one ought to be able to bump off a loved one with a packet of sleepers, washed down perhaps with a massive overdose of electric soup, this dream rather went over my head, but Margaret continued to read her papers unheeding, and Baker bowed his way backwards out of the Presence, still muttering about speculation now mercifully allayed.

Our major social event of the season has been the arrival of Basil Bush's Number Two, a moon-faced buffoon by the name of J. Danforth Quayle, here to celebrate – would you believe? – the hundredth anniversary of the birth of General Eisenhower, as feeble an excuse to get rid of an embarrassing subordinate as ever I came across. (It reminds me of the time Prosser-Cluff sent his wife back to Blighty to look up his family tree for the Burmah Magazine.) J. Danforth appeared on our doorstep in a flicker of flashbulbs, accompanied by two bespectacled assistants carrying briefcases and a portable fax machine. 'Mrs Thatcher,' trilled the First Minder, 'may I introduce J. Danforth Quayle, Vice President of the United States? Shake hands, Sir.' There was a moment's pause while this idea registered in the Vice President's blue eyes, then he took my hand and said: 'Guten Tag, Herr President! Did I get that right, Marvin?' I could tell from the expressions on the faces of his two attendants that this was not the best of starts, but within minutes he had identified the Boss, and was chatting naturally to her about the respective merits of his two ball-point pens, one of which you pressed, the other you screwed, he thought, in an anti-clockwise direction.

Marvin Troop did most of the talking over dinner, explaining the Vice President's firmly-held views on German Reunification, and the importance of Great Britain playing a fearless role in support of United States policy in the NATO alliance. Danforth munched away through all this, explaining that he was 'very careful about what he put in his body' and then, in a lull over the After Eights, launched unsteadily on a few reflections of his own. 'My understanding of the research material, Prime Minister, is that your lame duck role has been the subject of intense media speculation, suggesting that you may be, um, relinquishing your responsibilities in the foreseeable future, and we could be dealing with some Commie.' I could see that Marvin and his friend were not happy men, and the conversation was rapidly brought back under their control. 'What the Vice President is saying essentially,' intoned the second minder, Thackeray Golightly Jnr, 'is that the US looks to you, Prime Minister, as the beacon of liberty, the most stable factor in the Western Alliance.' At this, J. Danforth's jaw had visibly fallen, and he repeated the word 'beaker' several times before turning to Marvin and saying, 'Hey, that's not what you guys told me on the plane.'

How was your Bank Holiday? Maurice fell asleep in the sun at Huntercombe and his toupee melted.

Yours on the rooftop,

DENIS

Dear Bill,

Did you get Maurice's prospectus? It seems to me to make pretty good sense. If you take a dekko at the Market Profiles on pp. 5–7 you'll see that, following the relaxation of the Race Laws, we anticipate a Soweto-led boom in consumer durables, especially lawnmowers and strimmers, and Maurice feels, very reasonably, I think, that we should be in there selling. For once the old boy got his act together, and the brochures for Pik SA (Soweto) plc were in place on the hall table when De Klerk and his lady blew in for a barbecue on Sunday.

Bell and Ingham fortunately admitted they weren't all that clued up on God's Own Country and, knowing my extensive business interests in the Cape, very decently allowed me and Picarda to have a say in the guest list. Based on Maurice's big initiative, we plumped for a very nice little man who runs Rio Tinto Zinc, some old chummoes from Burmah days, BP and ICI, all of whom, I need hardly say, saw the logic in Maurice's argument and went for it like a bull up a drainpipe. Two safe reptiles were allowed out of their tank for the day: the little johnny with the toupee who edits the *Daily Mail* and a very sound man from the *Sunday Telegraph* who created a bit of an incident with one of the waitresses after I'd refilled his glass once too often.

De Klerk himself seems nice enough, if a bit too far to the Left for my liking. I can see why PWB tore up his membership card after seeing his life's work entirely buggered up by the new M.D. However, if it means more Krugerrands dropping in the hat every time we shake the tree, I suppose we must put up with it. Mrs Van der K. rang just before he arrived, blind with hysteria at the idea of the Boss and me sitting down at table with the Great Satan, and I can see that if you live there, the prospect of having Mrs Mandela living next door and playing her ghetto blaster into the small hours must give one pause.

On a lighter note, I enjoyed your joke about Mad Cow Disease, though it is not entirely original. Some old boy in the

'. . . *The sight of Gummer cramming a hamburger into his little mite's mouth* . . .'

Club asked me a few weeks ago if my nearest and dearest had been exposed to infection. However, now that it's a full-blown Edwina Currie number, the Boy Gummer has been cutting a very comic figure in an attempt to cling on to the NFU vote. The sight of Gummer cramming a hamburger into his little mite's mouth as the cameras whirred cannot have done much to restore confidence in our national dish. You probably remember that Headman who ran the Native Canteen for Prosser-Cluff who was convinced the Labour were trying to poison him with his own corned beef and kept a food taster. Prosser-Cluff was very amused by the expression on his face as he watched the taster the day they finally got him.

I bumped into that little greaser from the wireless, David Jacobs, coming in the other morning for another 'session' with

Margaret. Bell has decreed that she can only recapture the electoral high ground with a softer, more caring remix of her old brand image, and this involves her reading lavatory paper commercials into a tape recorder once a week while the erstwhile maestro of Any Questions? suggests soothing improvements.

After some fairly hairy moments in the wind tunnel, the new prototype was tested on Woman's Hour, where the Boss was questioned by one of the Militant Lesbos about the role of the working mother. I had some trouble keeping a straight face, I must admit, as I sat behind the glass with all the other Lesbos knitting their CND T-shirts. 'Whatever you do,' M. simpered, on a note that made the little dials in the control room quiver something horrible, 'try to set aside one afternoon a week for the sake of your little ones. It makes so much difference to their sense of being *loved* – do you know what I mean? – and *important* to their Mum!' When I recalled the Boy Mark at the age of four already programmed to transfer his own frozen supper from the deep freeze to the microwave I had to allow myself a wry smile.

All this activity on the image front is designed to counteract the Smellysocks' Summer Campaign. According to our Fashion Correspondent (Tarzan) who got a leaked copy in advance, this will be the New Arthur Scargill Look, though in fact, according to Boris who knows what he's talking about and isn't trying to terrify everyone into voting for him, it's all middle of the road stuff, Margaret's old ideas retailored 'with a human face'. Stand by for the Dirty Tricks Brigade. Benn is already in the cellars at Tory Party Central Office being injected with the Truth Drug prior to being released into the community to wreak his terrible revenge on poor Pillock. A propos, how can Ginger Nuts put up with that awful Glenys?

Have you seen this Wooster thing on the TV? It's good to have a series about real people for a change.

Yours bullishly,

DENIS